14 Days

AUG 20 '66
DEC 19 '66
OCT 4 '68
MAY 7 '73
JUL 15 '77
MAR 14 '79
NOV 6 '79
FEB 22 '80
AUG 25 '82
AUG 6 1985
SEP 3 1996
MAR 3 1 1997
OCT 1 4 '08

WITHDRAWN

THE MYSTERY MONSTERS

During the decade of the world's greatest scientific achievements, earthbound man still faces many unsolved mysteries about the creatures which share his own planet.

Not all the creatures that mystify us are monsters. Who can say that a possum or a worm or a clam can be labeled "monster"?—except when you consider sizes in relation to other species.

We know there are whales, but we do not know the maximum size of the largest species of whale. Monsters have been reported in large inland waters such as Flathead Lake in Montana and Loch Ness in the highlands of Scotland. Some of us are not sure such monsters exist; most of us are positive they do not. But no one has yet proved they do—or don't.

THE MYSTERY MONSTERS

BY GARDNER SOULE

G. P. Putnam's Sons   New York

For Janie

© 1965 by Gardner Soule
All Rights Reserved
Published simultaneously in the Dominion of Canada by Longmans Canada Limited, Toronto
Library of Congress Catalog Card Number: 65-13313
PRINTED IN THE UNITED STATES OF AMERICA
10216

CONTENTS

1. The World's Most Mysterious Animals — 7
2. The Heaviest Whale Ever Weighed — 13
3. The Wildest Dog — 25
4. The Flathead Lake Monster — 37
5. The Cat We Can't Catch — 56
6. The Yale Monster — 63
7. Found Alive—After 1,200 Years! — 77
8. "It Has the Death Ray" — 83
9. The Possum That Played Dead 50 Years — 97
10. The Soay Beast — 105
11. The Great Groaning Worms — 122
12. The Young Sea Serpent — 132
13. The Bear's-Paw Clam — 138
14. Our First Animals from Outer Space? — 148
15. Many More Mysteries — 168

Bibliography — 188

O Lords of the jungle,
wherever you roam.
—RUDYARD KIPLING
The Overland Mail

THE WORLD'S MOST MYSTERIOUS ANIMALS

*H*e is one of the United States's greatest experts on animal life in the sea. Yet he was completely baffled. Here he was, aboard a ship on the Atlantic, just off New Jersey. And there it was: a big animal, close at hand, heaving on the surface of the sea.

And he didn't recognize it—didn't know what it was, and doesn't—to this day.

The expert who was stumped by an encounter with a monster of the deep is Dr. Lionel A. Walford. His job is that of director of the Sandy Hook Marine Laboratories of the Bureau of Sport Fisheries and Wildlife of the Department of the Interior. He has used many years of his own experience and study to produce a thick book, *Living Resources of the Sea,* that in its field is a standard work. It is a book men refer to when they want to know something about sea life.

There is nothing in Dr. Walford's book, however, about the mysterious creature he was looking at. It appeared long and thin, like a sea serpent might.

"It resembled a transparent sea monster," Dr. Walford afterward said. "It looked like so much jelly. I could see no bones and no eyes, nose, or mouth. But there it was, undulating along, looking as if it were almost made of fluid glass."

Dr. Walford said it was about 40 to 50 feet long, and from 5 to 7 inches in diameter. Other witnesses said it was much bigger.

Other witnesses—there was a whole boatload of them. Altogether, there were seventy-six knowledgeable witnesses, including Dr. Walford, aboard the eighty-five-foot research vessel *Challenger* when the transparent unknown animal was sighted. These men are all either scientists or skin divers or sailors or fishermen—men thoroughly familiar with life in the ocean. They were all out there studying how waste matter dumped into the ocean affects the life in it.

The unknown animal puzzled them all. Not one of the men on the *Challenger* stepped forward to identify the mystery monster. Not one of them had even the remotest idea what it was.

Shortly thereafter, the monster was seen again. It appeared in an area of the sea called the Mud Hole, off Asbury Park, New Jersey.

The second appearance of the unknown did not make it any better known. It remains a total mystery.

Now these events might not have been surprising if they had happened a hundred years ago to one of the early explorers of Africa. At that time, and in an unexplored region, a man might come upon something huge and new and strange. But Dr. Walford and his associates met their mystery monster recently: on July 18, 1963. They did not have to travel far into the unexplored reaches of the ocean to find it—they were right offshore, very near New York City and Philadelphia and lying just a few miles from one of the most populated regions on earth, the U.S. East Coast.

You would expect that by today we would be sure we knew all the big animals on the globe. We don't. There are a number of puzzling, rarely seen beasts that, like the shimmering snakelike creature not far from the New Jersey beaches, are mystery monsters—never caught, never killed, never identified by men.

You might think that these rumored, ghostlike animals didn't exist—they sound too much like fairies. But scientists all the time keep catching up with and finding such mystery monsters and proving they are, after years of rumors, real after all. The young Charles Darwin, for instance, once found an unknown animal in one of the oddest ways I know: He ate it. Near the tip of South America, he consumed, without thinking, a strange fowl. Then he wondered what it was. He examined the leftover head, neck, legs, wings, and feathers. That was how the world for the first time got to know there was such a thing as the big bird today known as Darwin's rhea.

A cat is responsible for our knowing about a smaller, once unknown animal. In the 1890's, at a lighthouse on Stephens Island in New Zealand's Cook Strait, the lighthouse keeper's pet pussy brought in a small, brown, wrenlike bird that today is called *Traversia lyalli*. The cat brought in nearly a dozen specimens. No man—and no cat since—has ever caught another, and the wren has not been seen again. It may be extinct. At any rate, the cat is responsible for everything we know about *Traversia lyalli*.

In this book I recount the stories of other mystery monsters, recently discovered: a possum, out in Australia, that hid out for half a century; a sea serpent—or at least its child—dredged up by a great Danish sea scientist. And there are other mystery monsters, whose stories are told here, that are still hiding out and have not yet been corralled: In the heart of the U.S., a large creature, so far immune to human fishermen, troubles the waters of Flathead Lake, the biggest lake in the Rocky Mountains. In Australia, an unknown tiger-cat prowls, usually by night. Near Scotland recently, a new and unexpected mystery monster was spotted—for the first and only time. This happened when two men, out fishing in a small boat, had the most astonishing adventure any casual fishermen have lived through in recent years. The men encountered, at close hand, a giant unknown sea creature. The animal swam almost up to their boat, then swam away. Later, they described it in detail. No scientist can identify it.

There is another kind of mystery monster: animals that are identified, but that still are surrounded by mystery. We want to find out a great deal more about such creatures. The stories of some of the major mystery monsters in the animal world today are included in this book. Whales, for instance—you'd think we'd have them completely taped, we've caught so many hundreds of thousands of them. Not at all. Our ignorance is whale-sized. We haven't yet found out how to get whales to tell us how big they grow—but we do know about the heaviest one we've weighed. We can't explain why a mysterious dog—not the lion, not the leopard, not the crocodile—is the bloodiest killer in Africa. But we're gradually piecing together the story of the wild dog. We don't know much about the manta ray, the biggest of all the rays, a dweller near the surface of the open ocean. But Yale University men caught a monstrous one not long ago. We know more about the electric eel than we used to, but from this almost-unknown animal—it lives in only one jungle area on earth—we'd like to know how it develops electricity. In some ways, it produces power better than we can. We'd like to know practically everything about some of the biggest worms on earth—the serpent-sized monsters that make Australia's ground rumble and shake. The biggest shellfish on earth —the bear's-paw clam—apparently can kill men. But does it? And there is a bone-jarring question right now about some of the most exotic mystery monsters of all: the animals our spacemen may one day meet when they step onto the moon or Mars. Have we, or have we not, already actually gazed upon our first life from space? Have we, or have we not, found chemicals produced by such life—in effect, its bloodstains? And have we in our hands an animal that has lived for over a millennium —or for a total of twelve hundred years?

"The number of new animal species discovered each

year," says the National Geographic Society, "averages perhaps 50 mammals, 100 fish, 15 birds, and 5,000 insects."

The number of new facts found out about animals each year runs into hundreds of thousands.

This book tells of some of the unknown and uncaught mystery monsters that scientists would most like to get their hands on, and about some of the monsters surrounded by mysteries that scientists would most like to penetrate.

THE HEAVIEST WHALE EVER WEIGHED

How big do whales get? It's a simple question. The answer is even simpler: After hunting whales for centuries, and killing them by the tens of thousands, we do not know. The answer is a mystery.

The man who most recently tried to find out was Lieutenant Colonel Walden C. Winston of the U.S. Army. He measured and weighed—with some difficulty—a blue whale.

When you tried to scramble up the side of the whale, Colonel Winston wrote, it was as though you were climbing a hill.

The slaty bluish whale, dead, lay aboard the Japanese whaling ship *Hashidate Maru*. The date was January 27, 1948, two years after World War II. Colonel Winston was along on the whaling expedition, which had reached the Antarctic, as General MacArthur's representative in charge of the twelve-ship whaling fleet.

The blue whale, *Sibbaldus musculus* or *Balaenoptera musculus,* so far as we know is the biggest animal that ever lived. The greatest-sized monster of all time is alive, alive right now, and is pursued and hunted and caught in large numbers every year.

This may surprise you when you think of the huge dinosaurs that roamed (and lorded it over) the earth until about 70 million years ago. Fossil bones help us estimate that the 70-foot-long Brontosaurus weighed at least 30 tons. Branchiosaurus, another dinosaur, may have reached 50 tons.

The largest known living land animals, the elephants, are pygmies compared to the blue whale. An adult elephant often weighs 3 or 4 or 5 tons. But some far larger monster elephants—of up to 8 tons in U.S. circuses and 12 tons in Africa—have been known.

The blue whale is many times heavier and larger than any of these monsters, or any other that we have records of.

The first weighing of a blue whale—it's also called the sulphur-bottom, after the yellowish spots of diatoms often found on its belly—took place in 1903 in Newfoundland. Dr. F. A. Lucas, director of the American Museum of Natural History, found that it was 77 feet long and totaled 63 tons.

A Captain Sorlle at Stromness, South Georgia, near the Antarctic, weighed two others. A 66-footer totaled 53½ tons. An 89-footer, weighed on November 8, 1926, was 134½ tons.

Osmond P. Breland, the University of Texas's record

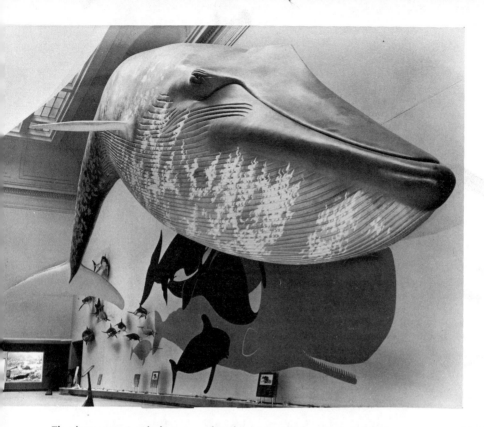

The hugest animal that ever lived is one of the most mysterious. That's the blue, or sulphur-bottom, whale. We do not even know how big it gets. This diving, 92-foot-long model is at the Smithsonian Institution.

keeper of the animal kingdom, wrote that the longest blue whale he heard of was 108 feet long and weighed 160,000 pounds (80 tons). He reported a shorter, 95-footer that tipped the scales at 294,000 pounds. Breland made his report before Colonel Winston's effort. So did J. R. Norman and F. C. Fraser of Britain, who wrote that the blue whale could reach 100 feet in length and 119 tons in weight.

But no blue whale ever had been weighed aboard ship. Colonel Winston and the Japanese planned to perform that job.

The monster first had to be caught. A catcher boat found one.

"At 1410 [2:10 P.M.]," Colonel Winston wrote, *"Kyo Maru No. 6* had fastened to a large blue whale. From the bridge of the ten thousand-ton factory ship, *Hashidate Maru,* we could see the catcher boat silhouetted against the horizon, creeping after her game like a fisherman playing a fighting pike, keeping a tight line, reeling in with huge winches.

"Presently from my position on the bridge I observed *Kyo Maru No. 6* drawing its game alongside to be inflated and towed, tail first, to the factory ship."

The factory ship's log that January 27 added:

"At 1705 [5:05 P.M.], Blue Whale, female, No. 319 was received on the flensing deck." The flensing deck is the place where the whales are cut up.

"The workmen," said Colonel Winston, "gathered around the gigantic mammal in awe."

But before the flensing, or cutting, and weighing of No. 319 began, Colonel Winston wanted to measure the whale and its parts in detail. This was when he discovered that clambering up the whale's sides was like hill climbing.

Colonel Winston wanted a big whale to measure. He had one. No. 319 provided him with measurements so startling as to be almost unimaginable.

The blue whale, R. B. Robertson wrote in *Of Whales and Men,* is "huge, immense, enormous, titanic, mighty,

THE HEAVIEST WHALE EVER WEIGHED

vast, stupendous, monstrous, gigantic, elephantine, mammoth, giant, colossal, Cyclopean, Gargantuan." Said a whaling inspector to Mr. Robertson, "If you're writing a book about a whaling expedition, don't tell the *exact* truth. If you do, nobody will believe you."

Nevertheless, here is the *exact* truth as revealed by Colonel Winston's measurements:

No. 319's total length was 89 feet (almost as long as a city lot).

From flipper to flipper across the back was 9 feet 6 inches. (It was as wide as a railroad passenger car.)

The whale's circumference was 43 feet 6 inches. (Its girth was that of a small submarine.)

Its tail flukes from tip to tip were 19 feet 10 inches (the length of a large living room).

Its lower jawbone was 22 feet 10 inches long (the length of a long limousine; an elephant could walk through this up-ended jawbone without touching at any point).

From tip of snout to blowhole was 17 feet 1 inch (a car's length).

The whale's eyes were 18 feet back of the tip of the snout.

Its flippers were 38 feet 6 inches behind the tip of the snout.

Each flipper was 9 feet 2 inches from tip to axilla (where the flipper joins the body).

Its head was 22 feet 8 inches long.

Its skull was 22 feet 5 inches long. It was 10 feet wide.

Once the measurements had been taken, the flensing and weighing of the whale could begin. The animal had to be weighed in hundreds of pieces because no scales aboard any ship could accept a load as heavy as a whale's. The job could be done at all only because the sea was calm, and the *Hashidate Maru,* well ballasted, was rolling only very slightly.

As flensing started, large strips of blubber came off the whale first. Altogether, there were around 20 tons of blubber.

"Huge, 11½-ton loins of rich, red meat peeled from the carcass," Colonel Winston reported, "ahead of spareribs weighing about 1.4 tons. A great mass of internal organs, weighing about 10 tons, spilled from the abdominal cavity."

The baleen (the whalebone in the mouth that strains the sea for krill, the shrimp that is the blue whale's principal food) came out—over a ton of it—and then the 3-ton tongue (in other words, the tongue alone weighed as much as some adult elephants).

The weight of the blood had to be estimated—at almost 9 tons.

Meat from the head weighed two tons; the stomach, half a ton; the heart, 950 pounds; the lungs, a ton; the liver, a ton. There were 18½ tons of bones and 22½ tons of whale oil.

All of this was weighed—bit by bit.

Chunks of blubber, meat, and bone, weighing 40 or 50 pounds each, were placed onto scales unable to handle over 200 pounds at a time. "Imagine," said Colonel Winston, "weighing a herd of cattle, piece by piece. . . . This is how we weighed the largest weighed whale in the world, totaling approximately 300,000 pounds!"

A whale can grow so large, some authorities believe,

because water supports its weight. The great size of the whale increase its muscular power. A 90-foot whale's tail flukes can develop as much as 520 horsepower. With this horsepower, a big blue whale can make 20 knots (a passenger ship's speed) when pressed, and can keep ahead of a 10-knot whaling ship all day.

There is an additional possible explanation for the huge size of the blue whale: Some scientists believe that in the case of an animal freed by the buoyancy of water from the pull of gravity, growth never really stops. They also believe that until growing does stop, aging does not begin. Therefore, a water beast may not age as land animals do, but may go on and on slowly getting bigger and bigger. Whether this is true or not is still unknown: one of the mysteries of the sea.

Another mystery about the blue whale has to do with one of its most conspicuous features. A series of grooves, two inches or so deep, runs lenghtwise along its throat and chest. You would think we would know all about them. We do not. The grooves may help remove hydrodynamic friction and thereby improve the swimming speed of the whale. Britain's Royal Navy has been experimenting with this idea. But so far we just don't know. "For almost a hundred years," writes E. J. Slijper in *Whales,* "scientists have vainly tried to discover the significance of the grooves."

Surrounding the blue whale and every other whale, there are some other truly whale-sized mysteries. For example, men have followed the whale into every sea, over hundreds of years, take thousands of the monsters every year, and are completely stumped for the answer to one of the simplest questions: How do whales sleep?

We know that cows, horses, and donkeys seem to doze rather than sleep as we do. Whales too? If so, do they doze floating at the surface, their blowholes clear of the water? Do they sleep for two hours, or perhaps in just fifteen-minute naps? "When we sleep," says Slijper, "our blood pressure and respiratory frequency drops, our muscles become relaxed, and there is a decrease in activity of certain nerve centers." The same things may happen to whales. They may not. We do not know.

What do whales drink, and how? The whale is a mammal like you. His body fluids—blood, lymph, oil, milk, etc.—are no more salty than those of a land mammal. They are not as salty as sea water. The whale doesn't sweat to get rid of salt; you do. His urine is no more salty than yours. There must be some organ in the whale's body that gets rid of salt from salt water, as an evaporator does the job on shipboard. Scientists never have found it. Meanwhile, the whale looks like an animal that must have fresh water to live, like any other mammal, and never gets anywhere near fresh water.

How intelligent are whales? How do you tell? Could you rig an I.Q. test for them? It is difficult to say the least; no one has done it; no one knows how. However, we think they communicate by sound. They almost talk to each other. Their relatives, porpoises, scientists today believe, converse back and forth with each other with such a variety of sounds that it is even remotely possible that one day men will talk to the porpoise, and vice versa; the porpoise today appears the wild animal man has the best chance to talk with. Similarly, whales probably talk. They probably use sound for another purpose: to locate objects in the water by a kind of asdic (or sonar).

Some experienced whalers think whales are learning. They believe that whales are much harder to catch than they were some years ago. This isn't only because there are fewer whales, but also because, when you come upon a pod of half a dozen, they make it far more awkward for a harpoon gunner to catch any of them than they used to. It used to be that a ship could stalk whales at low speed. Now propeller noises seem to be enough to send them running for the horizon. The noises of a ship's asdic gear chase some whales away, or so some whale men assert. Now the whales that are learning, if they are, are not the whales that were hurt by a gun or harpoon; they are those that were not hurt. They have been, if they are learning, smart enough to link certain noises with danger.

The blue whale does not use its intelligence to attack man. Despite its size, it has far too small a throat to have swallowed Jonah, or to get down any other man, or a large fish, and is of no danger, ordinarily, to them. One June night in the 1930's, though, a blue whale may have caused an upsetting time to Captain Henry le Blanc and six of the crew members of his large motor schooner. They were off Brown's Bank, eighty miles from Nova Scotia. They had gone to bed. While only one sailor was on deck standing watch, the schooner was struck a heavy blow from below. The resulting shock tossed the vessel into the air and hurled all seven sleepers to the floor. The schooner fell back into the ocean on her beam ends (her side). She then rocked so violently while straightening herself up that the man on deck watch nearly fell overboard. The shock was so violent the men thought the schooner had been rammed by a large ship. Once on deck, they saw a large whale thrashing around. It disappeared. Apparently, it had risen to breathe directly beneath the schooner, and got about as big a shock as the men did when it bumped into the ship.

As you might expect of the world's largest monster, the blue whale roams all oceans from Arctic to Antarctic, and is even found at the equator—the seven seas are its swimming pool. Most blue whales are taken in the Antarctic, near the pack ice, where Colonel Winston's was found. Not far away, whalers find some blue whales (if that is what they are) in the Roaring Forties, an especially turbulent part of the ocean. There is a mystery here: These may be a different race. They are all apparently only 72 feet long, or shorter. As it is illegal to kill a blue whale under 70 feet long, biologists rarely get to study these whales of the Roaring Forties.

A blue whale calf at birth, the Smithsonian Institution reports, may be as long as 26 feet. It is nursed for about seven months and is weaned from its two-hundred pounds of milk a day only when it has attained a length of 50 feet—the only 50-foot-long baby in the world. It is not likely to live, the Smithsonian says, over twenty-five years.

There is a 92-foot model of the blue whale towering over the Hall of Oceanic Life at the Smithsonian Institution. There is a skeleton of a young one in the Raffles Museum in Singapore.

Wrote Colonel Winston: "It had required the efforts of eighty men about 3 hours and 45 minutes to flense, dismember, and weigh, part by part, this largest whale ever weighed. Twenty-five more men were working below in the processing section!"

The sweating men aboard the *Hashidate Maru,* when

The *Hashidate Maru* of Tokyo, Japan, is shown as she returned after the Antarctic whaling trip during which her men weighed the biggest animal ever taken. The U. S. Army photo was made April 10, 1948.

they finished the job, had figures that added up to a world's heavyweight record total: 300,707 pounds for a single animal.

In other words, their blue whale was as heavy as 35 to 50 adult elephants, or as heavy as 5 brontosauruses.

But this is by no means the largest blue whale ever caught, or ever to exist. British scientists figure the blue whale weighs about a ton and a half per foot. One female blue that was caught measured 113½ feet. At a ton and a half per foot, she would have weighed 170 tons.

Even Colonel Winston himself was not as impressed as he might have been with his figures. "Larger and heavier whales," he said "were caught by the same expedition but they were not weighed or recorded." He commented, "I knew we had a very large whale, but it looked lean to me. Unfortunately, I was right." So he had to be content with only one distinction: No. 319 was merely the heaviest whale, and heaviest animal, ever weighed in the world.

THE WILDEST DOG

Charles W. Hobley, an English official, had one of the most unnerving adventures of anyone with the wild dog of Africa—the hunting dog. He plucked a hunting dog's pup out of the grass. The pup squealed. The pup was answered. Quickly twenty-five hunting dogs surrounded Hobley and his safari.

The dogs advanced, retreated, advanced, yelped, rushed toward Hobley and the pup, backed away, came in again.

Hobley felt menaced. He was sure the dogs might attack any minute. He tossed the pup back to the pack. That called off the dogs. The wild dogs, having regained their pup, went off and left him alone.

Would the dogs have attacked Hobley? We do not know. That's only one of a flock of mysteries about the

African hunting dog. It's one of the hardest-to-catch animals in Africa, and almost impossible to keep in captivity. Common though it is, the wild dog has had, over the years, impressive success in avoiding hunters —and in keeping secret the facts about himself. Much of what we do know about it comes from a few eyewitness stories—and tantalizes scientists into wanting to learn more.

John Taylor (in *Pondoro, Last of the Ivory Hunters*, Simon and Schuster, New York, 1955) reported a chilling story about the hunting dog. Taylor camped by a water hole. Just before daybreak he heard a lion's roar choked off in the middle. He thought the lion was fleeing. He heard a pack of the dogs, an appalling din: "The grating snarls and roars of the lion were mingled with the yelps and worrying of the dogs."

Next morning, Taylor and his gunbearers found a dog with its skull smashed.

They found another with its ribs flattened, and still another with a broken back.

There were signs that two or three dogs had vanished into the grass, perhaps licking wounds.

Then they found pieces of the lion: a forepaw, the tuft of its tail, and the lion's head.

The most ferocious killer in Africa is not the lion, not the leopard, not the man-and-beast-eating crocodile. It is the hunting dog—a creature many persons do not even know exists.

The killer most feared by the animals themselves, with perfect reason because it is the most dangerous to them, is the hunting dog.

It's a dog so wild man has never tamed it, a dog the

The most rapacious animal in Africa (the greatest killer of game) is the wild, or hunting, dog. Its splotched pattern is never the same on two dogs. Exhibit at the American Museum of Natural History.

size of a collie—up to 24 inches high, up to 4½ feet long, 50 to 75 pounds in weight. Its Latin name, *Lycaon pictus*, is from the Greek Lycaon, or wolf dog. Its popular names are wild dog or hunting dog.

Black and white and tan (or ochre-yellow), spotted in no set pattern, for each animal is different, the wild dog hunts either by day or night, an unusual thing for an animal. *Lycaon* hunts in packs of 3 to 50 or 100. The 25 that harassed Charles Hobley is a common number.

Lycaon has long, strong legs; powerful thighs; batlike black-and-yellow ears, 5 inches long, stiff and erect; a strong head on a strong neck. Its skull is about eight-and-one-half inches long, or collie-sized. The face is almost always black up to the brown eyes, with the rest of the head yellow or khaki. The white-tipped tail is bushy. "Striking in form, color, and movement," reported an eyewitness observer, Mary L. Jobe Akeley, "and splendidly equipped for the murderous life he leads."

Lycaon has been called faster than the cheetah. This is doubtful, because, Colonel Richard Meinertzhagen says, the cheetah, a great cat, has been timed at 44 miles an hour on several occasions. The cheetah may reach 50 or 55 miles an hour. The cheetah, except possibly for one or two of the gazelles, is believed the fastest land animal in the world. But the hunting dog is reported to have lasting power, which the cheetah lacks. The dog can go for a long time at high speed.

The wild dog has been observed time and time again not to be afraid of beasts many times its size. A man named F. C. Selous, a great game hunter in Africa, saw a pack of wild dogs pursuing thirty or forty buffaloes— huge animals that the experienced hunter approaches with caution and uneasiness. The wild dogs stampeded the buffaloes. The thundering herd passed Selous. The dogs howled at the flanks of the herd. Selous thought the dogs easily could have separated a calf and devoured it.

Lewis Cotlow (in *Zanzabuku,* Rinehart & Company, Inc., New York, 1956) described the pursuit tactics of the wild dogs: "When they are chasing a fast antelope, baying like real hunting hounds, they adopt a technique of community effort that no single animal can beat. One leader sets a very stiff pace, right behind the fleeing prey, while the others of the pack lag behind a bit. When the leader tires he drops back and another takes over. When the antelope begins to falter, all the dogs come alongside and slash with their teeth at the flanks of the doomed animal, ripping the skin until the intestines come out." The dogs slash away at the tormented animal till it keels over. Then they tear it to bits.

Besides antelopes, the hunting dog kills almost every game animal in Africa except the elephant, hippopotamus, and rhinoceros, and possibly excluding the zebra. Why not the zebra is one of many mysteries that surround the wild dogs. But Theodore Roosevelt reported that the zebra seemed unaffected by the wild dog, and for some reason did not much notice it. Mr. Roosevelt wanted zoologists to make a study of the zebra-dog relationship, and find out if the zebra was immune to attack, and, if so, why.

Natives of Africa have insisted they have seen the dogs drive lions off the lions' own fresh kill. Large packs of dogs are reported to have overcome lions, by others as well as by John Taylor. The natives, who give the dogs a wide berth, think they kill men. Others are not so sure. "I've never heard," Mr. Cotlow said, "of wild dogs attacking a human being."

Mary L. Jobe Akeley wrote that *Lycaon,* without hesitating, attacks the greater koodoo, an antelope the size of a bull. The greater koodoo, Mrs. Akeley judges, is one of "the strongest, fleetest, and most magnificent of African animals." It stands 5 feet high at the shoulder. It has long, spiral horns known to measure 5 feet 3 inches, a formidable weapon. A hunter considers even an average head a rare prize. Against a pack of dogs, Mrs. Akeley felt, the greater koodoo had no chance at all.

Mrs. Akeley was the wife of Carl Akeley, the American who brought so many animals back from Africa and who was largely responsible for the magnificent displays of African animals in New York City's American Museum of Natural History.

"These great dogs," Mrs. Akeley reported, "pursue and kill other large antelope, the kongoni, the waterbuck, and even the eland, the largest of the African antelope, the bulls of which run to a full ton in weight."

Other antelopes that are victims of the hunting dogs are the impala, Grant's and Thomson's gazelles, the reedbuck, the steenbok, the little duiker, and the thirteen-inch-high dik-dik.

When *Lycaon* arrives anywhere in Africa, the other game departs. The animals, sometimes even the lions, get right out of there. The country becomes empty of game, and a human hunter finds no pickings. A couple of days later, when the dogs have gone, the country is full. The animals come back, plus large numbers from whatever territory the dogs are prowling now.

Some scientists believe that Australia's dingo is the world's oldest dog and gave rise to all others. Is it? "Certainly," says Bill Beatty in *Unique to Australia*, "the dingo is a mystery animal."

The animals that flee are terrified. They ought to be. The hunting dog is one of the few animals that appears to kill indiscriminately, to kill far more than it needs for food, "for the joy of tearing flesh and spilling blood," Alexander Lake says. The hunting dog, writes Mary Akeley (in *Lions, Gorillas, and Their Neighbors,* Dodd, Mead & Company, New York, 1932), "has all the rapacity of his larger kinsman, the wolf. His blood lust is insatiable. He is indefatigable in the chase. Not content with killing reasonably for food, as do the other carnivora, he devotes his life to ruthless attack and wholesale slaughter. He is, therefore, far and away the worst foe of game in all Africa."

Peter Molloy (in *The Cry of the Fish Eagle,* Michael Joseph, London, 1957), reports that he was staying in a rest house in Africa when a pack of dogs arrived. "Antelope," Peter Molloy says, "bolted wildly in all directions, while the pack picked out their victim and settled on its trail, running it to exhaustion and tearing at its flanks and belly till it dropped. One kob [an antelope], eyes glazed with terror, flung itself into the crocodile-infested lake and swam to safety on the northern bank, miraculously unharmed."

If the animals are afraid of the wild dog, he is certainly not afraid of them—or of man. Instead, he is intensely curious. He has been known to stand up on his hind legs if the grass interferes with his vision and then jump up and down in an effort to get a better view of a man.

Puppies are born, seven or eight or ten of them, in large burrows often located on the grassy plains. Like their parents, the pups give off a revolting odor. The stench is stronger when the dogs are excited, and many men have gagged on it. A whiff may be the thing that warns other animals the dog is entering their territory. A man smells the dogs long before he sees them.

Although the hunting dog doesn't exactly bark, neither is he entirely voiceless like the tame Basenji dog of the Congo. The Basenji, which first arrived in the U.S. as recently as 1937, is barkless. *Lycaon's* sounds have been described variously: as peculiar cries that sound more like a flock of owls than meat-eating animals; as coughing, sighing sounds; as a monkey's chatter; as a cuckoo's note; as a horse's whinny; as "ho-ho-ho-ho"; as wolflike howling, repeated rapidly, sometimes answered from a distance; as a hoarse cry that sounds like a baboon or bushbuck.

There are other wild dogs in the world: The largest of all, the National Geographic Society reports, is the wolf, *Canis lupus,* which lives in Europe, Greenland, and North America. The American eastern timber wolf, *Canis lupus lycaon,* is a form of gray wolf. Other wild dogs include the dingo of Australia, the dhole of India, and the bush dog of South America, once believed extinct but found, since 1933, to be still in existence. Another wild dog in South America has been rumored, but never caught by zoologists. In Africa, natives say that, besides *Lycaon,* a smaller, black wild canine exists, but this one too is unproved by science. Some more hunting expeditions must be made before we can be sure we have made the acquaintance of all the dogs in the world.

A flock of mysteries surrounds the wild dog, and makes it a little-known animal. They may be puzzles for some time yet. The wild dog, not being lovable or likable, is not easy to study. Men have tried to tame it, but it stays wild. One of the few zoos the wild dog has been in is the one in Dublin, Eire (Ireland). There, at the sight of blood from a wound on its leg, one of the dogs got frantic and chewed off its own paw. The hunting dog is so fast you can't catch it and so nimble you can't get a good shot at it. As a result, few exhibits of mounted wild dogs are to be seen. One of the few displays of hunting dogs is at the American Museum of Natural History in New York City.

Some of the mysteries around the hunting dog: What are its natural enemies? Lions may kill a few dogs, and other animals—leopards, eagles, vultures—may perhaps make off with some young. Driver ants may wipe out a few pups. If its enemies are no more plentiful than those we know, why hasn't the hunting dog eaten up all the animals in Africa, and overrun the continent?

Another puzzle: What good does it do? Possible answers: drives grazing animals out of an area—and on to better feeding grounds. It may weed out the unfit animals. It may control species of antelope that otherwise would multiply too rapidly for their food supplies. Another stumper: Does *Lycaon* kill, as is rumored, almost only male animals? Only very rarely has it been reported to dispatch a female animal. Still another question: What exactly is the relationship of the African wild dog to the wild dogs of other continents? And to your own pet?

A baroness from Denmark, Karen Blixen, who wrote *Out of Africa* (Random House, Inc., 1937, 1952) under the pen name of Isak Dinesen, reported a sight of the hunting dogs like nothing anyone else has experienced. She was out way ahead of her safari, trekking over grass country with only her African servant Farah. She and

Farah saw not the common pack of two dozen wild dogs, but, she estimated, five hundred together. This is the only time, apparently, a number anywhere near this big ever has been seen.

One of the most surprising eyewitness accounts of hunting dogs, a story from the Congo, was recounted by John Hillaby over the BBC (British Broadcasting Corporation) not long ago. Mr. Hillaby's tale is enough to show that whatever we will learn about the wild dogs will be startling. He observed their strict discipline—even when the dogs were tired and hungry. "One afternoon, about two o'clock, we were driving along very slowly in the jeep, when my host, who had been a white hunter, saw a pack of fourteen of the dogs, sitting quietly on the top of the slope overlooking a big plain. . . . He drove round them in slow, ever-diminishing circles until we were literally right among them. . . .

"Another *Lycaon* was streaking across the plain towards them and us. It was apparently a scout dog. The others rushed down to meet it. There was a great deal of frantic tail-wagging and nose-rubbing, and then all fifteen of them rushed off on what was apparently a hunt. We followed. I think I have never been more jolted in my life. . . . After about twenty minutes, we came across the quarry, an antelope, an impala, which had been skillfully isolated from the rest of the herd so that it could not run fast or far. Then it was struck down, ripped open, and killed. I have no wish to dwell on the scene except to say that around it were fifteen of the bloodiest-looking dogs I have ever seen.

"According to the books the animals should have gone absolutely crazy over that meal. But not at all. They formed a queue. The king dog, or leader, took first place. There was no shoving. He ate his fill. His [mates] came next and the whole troop followed in ones and twos until the meanest dog in the pack, a lame beast at the rear, came up and got what he could. It was an orderly caste system among animals which are reputed to be among the fiercest in the world. When they had finished, there was nothing left of that impala but the horns and skull on which a few yellow butterflies were beginning to settle. The dogs were dozing."

That strict discipline can be practiced by worn-out, ravenous wild animals is hard to believe. But we have a lot to learn about the African hunting dog—the wildest dog in the world—as we have about many other animals.

THE FLATHEAD LAKE MONSTER

"It was a horrible looking thing," Mrs. Gilbert Zigler said, "with a head about the size of a horse . . . and about a foot of neck showing."

Mrs. Zigler, who lives in Polson, Montana, had just seen the Flathead Lake monster.

She thus became another of a long line of eyewitnesses who, standing near the edge of Flathead Lake, the greatest natural fresh-water lake between the Mississippi River and the Pacific Ocean, have watched an animal they cannot explain.

The Flathead Lake monster is a large, entirely unknown animal that has been seen by many persons yet caught by no one. What animal or fish it is is a mystery. It is a current mystery—now playing. Mrs. Zigler saw the creature in 1960. Others saw it in 1961, 1962, and 1963.

It may be of a familiar species—or an entirely un-

A major mystery: What is the largest freshwater fish? Men have lived on rivers and lakes for centuries—and do not know. One candidate is the pirarucu of South America. This specimen is at Harvard.

known one. At first, around 1920, the creature was called a sea serpent. Now it's usually referred to as a "big fish."

"If you're ever around Polson, on Flathead's south shore," Paul H. Fugleberg, editor of the *Flathead Courier,* wrote in *The Spokesman-Review,* Boise, Idaho, "stop, and start asking around about the 'Flathead monster.' You'll hear some of the doggonedest, most mystifying conglomeration of fish stories that ever registered on an eardrum.

"If you're like most folks, you'll listen to reports of superfish sightings with tongue in cheek and one eye winking at your pardner.

"But after the third or fourth go 'round, you'll suddenly realize that these folks aren't just flapping their gums, trying to amuse a tourist with tall tales. By golly, they've seen something that really does defy description and explanation in the shimmering blue Flathead Lake."

For instance, on Saturday, June 15, 1963, a whole dozen persons at one time saw the USO (Unidentified Swimming Object) in Flathead Lake. Saturday is, of course, a day when a good many people can get to the lake, and a dozen is something of a crowd for a territory as sparsely populated as that section of Montana.

Joe and Helen Stevens, of the Finley Point store, said that the Saturday onlookers saw, off Finley Point, what appeared to be a large log floating toward the main part of Flathead Lake. They thought it was being towed by a motorboat. They looked again, but there was no boat. Then the object moved in an undulating—rising-and-falling—fashion as had been reported in earlier sightings.

On a sunny Sunday, September 8, 1963, two Polson high school teachers, Miss Heather McLeod and Mrs. Genevieve Parratt, were in a small outboard boat in Skidoo Bay. They saw, about 11:30 A.M., "a dark gray object with three humps." The object was cruising from shallow water to the center of the lake. About ten feet of its length, the women estimated, were visible. A second boat frightened the thing. It submerged, came up again, and headed for the main part of the lake. It left a large boatlike wake behind, and the humps appeared and disappeared in a rhythmic, undulating manner.

Both Miss McLeod and Mrs. Parratt said they had

never seen anything like it before. Both said they had scoffed at previous reports of the denizen of the Flathead deeps, but are now "believers."

After this story became known, Mrs. Wade Vincent and Mrs. Richard Burbank said that on the same day they'd seen a ten- or twelve-foot object that seemed to dip and glide, to submerge quickly, and to leave a wake. They had kept silent before, for fear of not being believed.

Almost a year before, in July 1962, a car with California license plates screeched to a stop on the wooden bridge that spans the Flathead River, which enters the lake at Polson. Its occupants jumped out and rushed to the railing to stare at a glistening, black object they could not identify. It was moving *against* the steady current. It moved with a smooth, undulating, up-and-down motion.

A car driven by a Polson housewife drew up. One of the Californians gasped, "What on earth do you have in this lake?"

Answered the equally startled housewife, "I don't know. I've heard of the Flathead monster for years, but this is the first time I've seen it."

The monster swam away, picking up speed as it did.

A water-skier on Flathead Lake, also in 1962, was skiing along, when a huge fish leaped out of the water right next to her. She lost her balance and fell. The most popular theory was that she saw a Mackinaw trout—a fish that grows up to forty pounds in weight and is common in Flathead Lake. But was it a Mackinaw?

Two lads the Flathead Lake monster caught up with, in a sense, were Ronald and Maynard Nixon. They

Pirarucu or *Arapaima gigas*, here being unloaded at Harvard by Dr. Giles Mead and Joseph O'Leary, may reach 15 feet long, and hundreds of pounds in weight. But a neighbor in South America, a catfish, may be larger.

poked fun at the idea of the creature. They thought it was a myth and so ridiculous that they faked pictures of it, doing things like painting pictures of dinosaurs onto photos of the lake, or drawing dinosaurlike heads sticking up above the surface.

They had their fun pretending those were pictures of the unknown.

Then the monster got revenge.

The Nixons were driving along the Polson waterfront. They saw in the water a strange thing they did not recognize. They stopped. They stared.

Later, Ronald Nixon said, "We had a good view, looking down on the water from only about three hundred feet away. It was moving straight away from the shore and fast enough so the wave at the front was about two feet high. The wake at the back must have been at least twenty-five feet from the front, so the object must have been longer than that. There was no fin on the back. It couldn't have been a sturgeon. I don't have any idea what it was."

On a mild December day in 1962, two Polson men were trolling for Mackinaw on Big Arm Bay. One quietly told his partner to stop the engine of the boat and reel in his line. Then he told him to look about halfway between the boat and the shore and tell him what he saw.

"Looks like some big, long, black thing," the second fisherman replied. "It must be a log."

"Can't be a log," the first fisherman said. "It just popped up there all of a sudden."

As the boat drifted quietly, the long, black object stayed motionless, just like a log. The men decided to go in for a closer look. They started their engine. That did it. As they swung the boat around, the object came to life and swam away, leaving a long, boatlike wake behind it.

Whatever it is, the Flathead Lake monster provides Flathead Lake with a story to compare with that of Loch Ness, Scotland. In Loch Ness, people keep observing a huge, unknown animal that—just like Mrs. Zigler's Flathead Lake monster—often displays a head about the size of a horse's, together with a length of neck. By today, several thousand persons have seen the Loch Ness monster—one of the world's most famous unidentified beasts.

Loch Ness is in the heart of the Highlands of Scotland —right in the middle of the country and away from the sea. Flathead Lake also is inland. It is located on the western edge of Montana, near the long, thin portion of Idaho.

Loch Ness, 24 miles long, is Scotland's longest lake. Flathead Lake is much larger. It is 38 miles long, north to south, and from 5 to 15 miles wide. Loch Ness could easily support a monster, scientists have shown, or a series of monsters. The food is there, mainly fish. There is not the slightest need for scientists to test Flathead Lake so far as fish life is concerned. Flathead Lake is a fisherman's paradise. Its 120,000 surface acres abound with cutthroat, Mackinaw, rainbow, and Dolly Varden trout; salmon; whitefish; bass; and perch.

All around it the story is the same: Nearby reservoirs provide bass, perch, catfish, and trout; glacier-fed lakes offer more trout. In the winter, fishing goes right on, sometimes through the ice, both on Flathead Lake and the reservoirs. Actually the lake is so well supplied with fish that it is open the entire year to fishermen. There never is a closed season.

There is far more game around Flathead Lake than there is around Loch Ness. There is, in fact, some of the finest big-game hunting in the U.S. Elk, deer, brown and black bear are in the area. Wild-fowl hunting is for Chinese pheasant, for duck, and for ruffed grouse, Franklin grouse, and blue grouse. The bird and game population is protected. A nearby United States Wildlife Refuge, since its opening in 1921, has sheltered 134 species of birds. South of the lake there is located the National Bison Range, established in 1908. Today it has about five hundred bison, plus elk, mule deer, white-tailed deer, bighorn sheep, and antelope.

The wild, primitive land around Flathead Lake is about the only part of the U.S. left, except Alaska, in which you can pursue that most dangerous of North American wild animals, the grizzly bear. Montana's grizzly-bear population is the largest of any state's, again excepting Alaska. Few states have any known grizzlies at all.

The landscape around Flathead Lake is the kind whose grandeur you associate, in your mind, with the U.S. West and with grizzly-bear hunting. It is a spectacular landscape, the kind a man stares at and never gets over, no matter how long he lives; the kind of scenery that is magnetic and helped attract our ancestors in their covered wagons to keep rolling toward the west. Surrounding the lake, reservoirs, and streams, and the Flathead River, are the Rocky Mountains. The Missions are to the east, towering sheer from the valley floor up to sharp, magnificent peaks seven thousand feet above the small

Mystery of American rivers and lakes is the garfish. Could it be the Flathead Lake Monster? Gars come in 10 species; may reach 12 or even 20 feet; are slim, can move fast. A peculiarity: Their bones are green.

town of Polson (population only 2,315). Other snow-covered mountains are to the west. The sunrises and sunsets alone are worth the price of a visit to Polson. The country between the mountains is mostly irrigated farm land. The farmers raise cattle and sheep and grow hay, small grains, and both sweet and sour cherries along the shore of Flathead Lake. Lumber is taken out of the mountains.

When, in September 1960, Mrs. Zigler observed the Flathead Lake monster, she was near a pier at the Polson country club's swimming beach. She, and her husband and son, Jim, saw what looked like a big fish thrashing about in the water.

The three Ziglers live in a home at the country club. Zigler is groundskeeper at the club during the summer, and a city policeman and part-time deputy sheriff the rest of the year.

It was at seven thirty on a Friday night when the Ziglers heard waves crashing against the shore of the lake.

They went out and looked. There were no boats churning the lake. Just the same, high waves were splashing against the shore. And something was sending water high over the end of the pier.

They saw the something at the end of the pier. It was rubbing against the pilings as if it were an animal scratching its back.

Zigler turned back to the house for a rifle.

Mrs. Zigler went closer to the pier. As she did so, she saw the monster raise its head out of the water. This was the moment when she saw the neck and horse's head and thought the creature looked "horrible."

She was frightened. She screamed. Her husband, now with his rifle in his hand, came running back.

By the time he got there, the big fish, or whatever it was, was swimming east, parallel to the shore, at a very fast speed, and, as the Loch Ness monster is also reported to do, making a very big wake.

Zigler tried to signal a boat that came into view. He wanted the boatman to pick him up and take him out for a closer look.

"I was waving my rifle around and he probably thought I was a crazy man or something," Zigler said, "and he stayed out a good distance and then went away."

The Ziglers and their boy all three were sure that what they saw was not merely clashing currents or boats' wakes or floating logs. What they saw definitely was a live animal, they said.

Paul Fugleberg, the editor of the *Flathead Courier,* told the story of the Ziglers in his issue of September 8, 1960. He also reported, because as editor he was in a position to hear about them, other recent sightings of the Flathead Lake monster.

The Ziglers' adventure, Fugleberg pointed out, was actually the second sighting of an unknown object in the area within two days.

On the Wednesday before the Ziglers saw the splashes and the big fish, Mrs. C. E. Blankenhorn, her father, and her daughter all saw "something large in size swimming against the current" near the outlet of a creek that runs by the eighth hole in the Polson country club's golf course.

Two weeks earlier still, George Garbes reported a "big

fish, probably a sturgeon" in the waters of Indian Bay, along the west shore of Flathead Lake.

The Flathead Lake mystery has, so far, lasted a long time.

Bob Lambeth, the fish and game warden in Polson, says that, in the late 1920's, fishermen, seining Flathead Lake for Lake Superior whitefish, reported that their nets were torn apart by giant-sized fish that could have been sturgeon. The nets, he says, were built to withstand forty-pound bull trout, but were shredded anyway.

The two principal schools of thought about the Flathead monster, Editor Fugleberg says, call it (1) a log, or (2) a sturgeon.

The sturgeon, although it is not known at present to exist in Flathead Lake, could be the monster. There are around twenty species of sturgeon. At least seven of them live in the U.S.

Sturgeons are both salt-water and fresh-water fish, and they grow large enough to be the monster in the lake. The white (or Transmontaine, Oregon, or Sacramento) sturgeon, for example, lives in the Pacific from Monterey, California, to Alaska, ascends the Sacramento and Fraser rivers, and is by far the biggest fresh-water fish in Alaska. It is reported to reach 13 feet in length and 1,000 pounds in weight. But it is so rare that only a very few ever have been caught. The official record for a white sturgeon taken on rod and reel was made in the West near Flathead Lake: On the Snake River, Idaho, on April 24, 1956, Willard Cravens hauled out a white sturgeon 360 pounds in weight, 9 feet 3 inches long, and 7 feet 2 inches in girth.

The record lake sturgeon caught on rod and reel was

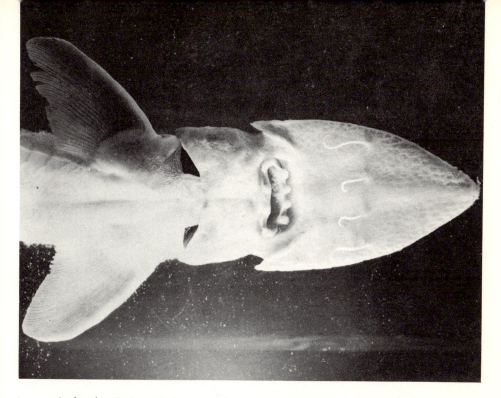

Is this the Flathead Lake Monster? This is a sturgeon—photographed from beneath—at the Miami Seaquarium, Florida. The Flathead Lake Monster, unidentified, is today's big Rocky Mountain animal mystery.

taken in Lake Huron in 1922. It weighed 225 pounds and was 7 feet 3 inches long. The paddlefish or spoonbill sturgeon, in the Mississippi Valley, gets to be 3 to 5 feet long. The Atlantic Ocean sturgeon approaches 12 feet in length and 500 pounds in weight. Overseas, the Russian white sturgeon, or beluga, or *huso* lives—according to one hard-to-believe report—for two hundred to three hundred years, and grows to a length of over 14 feet and to a weight of more than a ton. Russian sturgeons are most famous for a single product: caviar. This consists of the 2 to 3 million eggs a female lays each breeding season. Osmond P. Breland of the University of Texas says the record whopper of all Russian sturgeon weighed 3,221 pounds. One 26 feet long has been reported.

Sturgeons seem to be a changeable group of fishes. They may vary as they grow, and their forms tend to cross with one another at times. As a result, there is a difference of opinion among experts as to the number of species that actually does exist. In 1956, in Flathead Lake, a fish was caught that may have been a sturgeon. Some thought it was; some thought it wasn't. It started an argument, and the only thing that will settle the fishermen's quarrel is another specimen from the lake, the catching of the monster the Ziglers saw, for example. Several years ago, two professional sturgeon fishermen from Pasco, Washington, attempted for a week, without success, to drag a sturgeon out of Flathead Lake.

The fact that sturgeons are sluggish bottom-dwellers might help explain why the mystery monster at Flathead Lake is rarely seen. They swim slowly about, near the bottom. Sturgeons root about in sand or mud with their long snouts, and feel for their prey with sensitive feelers, or barbels, in front of their toothless mouths. Once a sturgeon has found its prey, it pushes out its mouth like a funnel. Into the mouth, the sturgeon sucks up worms, shellfish, crustaceans, fishes, aquatic plants, and plenty of mud. When upset, a sturgeon can swim rapidly. It often will come to the surface and leap clear.

In cold weather (of which there is plenty at Flathead Lake—the growing season between frosts lasts only 120 days) the sturgeon goes to sleep. It lies torpid. That would make it most likely to be spotted, as is the case with the Flathead Lake monster, in the summer. June, July, August, September, and October are the months when the Flathead monster is most often seen.

The Flathead Lake monster can, of course, be some other fish. Quite a splash could be made by creatures as small as the record Dolly Varden trout caught on rod and reel (32 pounds), taken in 1949 by N. L. Higgins, or the record rainbow trout or steelhead (37 pounds),

Sturgeon uses barbels (whiskers), *left*, to root along bottom for food. Sturgeon is largest anadromous (ascending rivers from the sea) fish in North America. A 1,285-pound, 12½-foot specimen has been caught.

taken in 1947 by Wes Hamlet. Both of these fish were caught in Lake Pend Oreille, Idaho. The monster could be a lake, or Mackinaw, trout grown large. The Mackinaw can grow from an ordinary fish into monster-size. The average Mackinaw, a common fish in Flathead Lake, weighs 4 to 5 pounds. But the record on rod and reel, caught by Hubert Hammers in Lake Superior, on May 25, 1952, weighed 63 pounds 2 ounces. Commercial fishermen have taken Mackinaws up to 125 pounds in weight.

The record fresh-water fish caught on rod and reel by U.S. anglers change almost as often as track-and-field records. The following list of American records, with their dates, shows, among other things, that our concepts of the sizes of the monsters in our lakes and rivers change frequently. Not all these fish are known in Flathead Lake, but the monster could be among them: A carp, 55 pounds 5 ounces, 42 inches long, 31 inches in girth, was caught July 10, 1952. A blue, or Mississippi catfish, 97 pounds, 57 inches long, 37 inches in girth, was caught September 16, 1959. A channel catfish, 57 pounds, 44.2 inches long, 32.8 inches in girth, was caught March 8, 1960. An alligator gar, 279 pounds, 93 inches long, was caught in 1951. A longnose gar, 50 pounds 5 ounces, 72¼ inches long, 22¼ inches in girth (a long, thin one), was caught in 1954.

I have another figure on a larger alligator gar: 302 pounds, almost 10 feet long. There once were stories that gars grew to 20 feet in length. Primitive, with long bodies, sharp teeth, and heads covered with bony plates, they would certainly qualify as ugly, as Mrs. Zigler described

Full-length view of sturgeon, by Miami Seaquarium. Sturgeon lives in Europe, the United States, Russia—and maybe in Flathead Lake. It also lives in the Atlantic, and in the Pacific from California all the way to Alaska.

the Flathead Lake monster. The alligator gar is known as far north as St. Louis.

A muskellunge, 69 pounds 15 ounces, 64½ inches long, 31¾ inches in girth, was caught in 1957. A northern pike, 46 pounds 2 ounces, 52½ inches long, 25 inches in girth, was caught in 1940. A cutthroat trout, 41 pounds, 39 inches long, was caught in 1925, one of our longest-lasting big-fish records.

I tried to find the answer to the question, "What is the biggest fresh-water fish in the world?" I don't suppose anyone yet knows for sure. But there are monsters in many areas. Four parts of the globe possess giant catfish: Africa and Asia have the schilbeid, 250 pounds in weight, 7½ feet long—a giant, toothless, plant-eater that very little is known about, a first-class mystery monster. Malaya, in its big rivers and deep pools, harbors the tapah, a catfish that may weigh 100 pounds and be over

5 feet long. It has formidable teeth, and pulls under swimming dogs. South America has a 3½-foot-long catfish, one of which was caught by a Theodore Roosevelt expedition, that grabs monkeys when the monkeys come down on low branches over the river to drink. The specimen captured by the Roosevelt expedition had a monkey inside it. South America also has rumors of the piraiba, a gigantic, grayish-white, 9-foot-long catfish with the proportionately big head of the catfish and the usual gaping mouth. Zoologists have never caught, or even seen, a piraiba, but Amazon River natives are so sure it will grab them, they build fences in the river to keep it out. The European wels is described as the biggest catfish of all: almost 13 feet long, 650 pounds in weight.

If you rule out the sturgeon, because it is both a salt- and fresh-water fish, one nomination for the biggest strictly fresh-water fish is the *Arapaima gigas,* or pirarucu, found in the Amazon and other South American rivers, where it is said to reach 10 feet in length and around 400 pounds. Two authorities say 15 feet. Both Yale and Harvard universities in recent years have obtained specimens. Harvard's specimen, 7 feet 2 inches long, is as long, Harvard says, as any *arapaima* "authentically recorded." It weighed 165 pounds.

The U.S. West, particularly rivers from central California northward, has the Colorado squawfish. It weighs up to 100 pounds, gets up to 6 feet long. It is, believe it or not, a minnow. It is the biggest minnow in the Western Hemisphere. India has a toothless monster, a carp called the mahseer, whose leathery mouth can crush tough freshwater snails and bend a spoon double. One 150-pound mahseer was reported (in H.S. Thomas's 1897 book, *The*

THE FLATHEAD LAKE MONSTER 55

Rod in India). It may get heavier. A man named Sanderson caught a mahseer and said: "It had a shoulder like a bullock, was 5 feet long and had a 3-foot-2-inch girth. I could only lift it a few inches off the ground with both arms."

J. F. McAlear, a real estate and insurance broker at Polson, is himself a fancier of the idea that the Flathead monster is a sturgeon. He has made a standing offer of $1,400 cash to the first angler to get a 14-foot-long fish in Flathead Lake. He offers $100 more for every foot of length over 14 feet. Editor Fugleberg offers $25 for the first photo of the monster. "Nobody who sees it ever seems to have a camera," he complains.

Besides being called a sturgeon or a floating log, or many other kinds of fish, the Flathead monster by today, Editor Fugleberg writes, also has been "identified" as a homemade submarine, an overweight skin diver, and a prehistoric dinosaur left over from the age of great swamps. (Scotland's Loch Ness monster also has been called some kind of prehistoric water-dwelling beast.)

Now, Mr. Fugleberg tells me, a new attitude is growing toward the monster on the part of many local people. These people know they can't explain it. They don't argue about it. They have adopted a wait-and-see-before-deciding attitude.

This new school was reinforced by 1963 sightings. On one occasion an object 15 feet or more in length was spotted in Skidoo Bay, on the east shore of Flathead Lake, and was watched for half an hour before it disappeared.

It could have been a log. It could have been a sturgeon. It could have been something else. The one thing sure is that we have to wait and see. The proof is not yet in.

THE CAT WE CAN'T CATCH

Camping south of Prosperine, Queensland, Australia, on June 5, 1957, Mrs. Joan Simms was resting on a cot in the back of a truck. Beside her was her Labrador dog. "As I was drifting off to sleep," Mrs. Simms remembers, "the dog disturbed me, growling softly. He continued uneasy, so I put out my hand to pat him—his hair was standing on end, his whole body aquiver."

Mrs. Simms suspected an intruding wild animal of some kind near the truck. The uninvited visitor may have been a mystery monster: a tiger-cat, reported for almost one hundred years to exist in Australia, but never yet captured or killed and identified by scientists. In *The Maybe Monsters* (G. P. Putnam's Sons; New York; 1963), I told of some of the animals no hunter has ever caught, and recounted some of the adventures Australians have had with their unknown tiger-cat. I have heard more of their stories, including that of Ted and Joan Simms, since that book came out.

Mrs. Simms had put out some scraps remaining after dinner. "I became conscious of something crunching the leftover chop bones," she says, "no more than seven feet from where we were sleeping. I roused my husband. It was obvious the dog was terrified. We watched quietly for some time."

But the Simmses could not identify the animal. Neither Ted nor Joan could make out for certain, in the dark, what the coloring of the animal was.

Whatever it may have been, Mrs. Simms recalled later, "it looked rather like a leopard. It was too big for a domestic or wild cat, more the size of a dog. Only it had short legs with pricked, pointed ears and a long tail. . . . My husband estimated its length to be approximately five feet from its nose to the tip of its tail."

That is about the usual size of the Australian tiger-cat as it has been described by many people who have seen it, or who believe they have. It appears to be a strange, furred animal, with a cat's head, long claws, large fangs, and stripes like a tiger's, and it is about as large as a medium-sized dog.

A Melbourne, Australia, man named K. Zeinert believes that the tiger-cat is a real animal and will some day be caught and identified. Mr. Zeinert not long ago asked an Australian newspaper, *People,* to ask its readers if any of them had seen the beast.

Some had. Australia's unknown tiger-cat is still on the prowl. Originally, it was believed to dwell mainly in the jungles of the Cape York Peninsula in Australia's

A rare animal is the small (about 18 inches long) Australian native cat. Native cat is so shy you can't tame it. It is gray or black with white spots. There may be a bigger, uncaught wild cat in Australia.

northeast corner. By today it has been spotted at many places up and down the whole eastern (Pacific) coast of Australia. It has been seen at least once in the southwest corner of Australia.

Most eyewitnesses obtain only a glimpse of the animal.

Mrs. Hugh Kennedy, one day near dusk, heard her dogs getting excited. She rushed out of her house. Near a fowl shed, no longer used, she saw a brown animal she at first thought was a fox. When it turned to face her and the dogs, she changed her mind.

"It was a large, catlike animal," her husband explained, "similar to the lynx. It was larger than my blue cattle dog, possibly 18 to 20 inches in height, tawny colored (no markings), with a long, smooth, catlike tail. The body was long, narrow and sleek.

"The most frightening part was the catlike head, small pointed ears, and terrific fangs. It hissed like a cat and used its front paws to keep off the dogs. Unfortunately, by the time the wife had returned to the house to get a rifle, the animal had vanished. However, it was afraid neither of dogs nor humans."

Alan E. Skiller of Seaford, Victoria, Australia, described the animal in pretty much the same way, except that he added that it has black stripes about two inches wide between flank and shoulder.

William Newton of Berrigan, New South Wales, was out shooting in Queensland, a long time—thirty-five years —ago, when he saw an animal that might have been the tiger-cat. Said he: "The dogs gave chase, but it eluded them easily. It crossed a sandy dry creek and I inspected its footprints, which were definitely those of an outsize cat."

Ten years ago, between Upper Colo and Singleton, New South Wales, Mr. Newton saw the mysterious tracks again. "The footprints were definitely the same as those I saw in Queensland," he says.

R. F. Brown of Randwick, New South Wales, says he actually trapped the tiger—and held it for a few minutes. He was out ferreting rabbits when a striped animal got into his net. He managed to hold on to the creature for five minutes, he says, but then his grip weakened and the tiger-cat escaped. He thought it weighed 50 to 60 pounds.

George Sumner of Port Hedland, Western Australia, says he actually shot the tiger-cat in 1905 near Katanning, southwest of Perth. He says it had a striped, gray and black body, short hair, and a catlike head. "I feel sure it was not a domestic cat gone wild," he says, "but like a fool I did not remove the skin and send it to a museum."

A man driving along the road from Beech Forest to Gellibrand, in Australia's Otway Range, not long ago saw what appeared to be a tiger-cat. He noticed a feline-like head and dark stripes that traveled toward the rear of the beast. He thought that the predominant color of the creature was dark fawn.

In the 1960's, near an Australian town called Emmaville, an intruding animal caused a flurry of excitement and worry by making off with many sheep. When, in one June-July period, it was reported to have killed seventy sheep, the excitement became downright alarm.

Local people say the beast, which was not caught, resembled a tiger.

One Emmaville man saw a strange animal in his headlights. It was two feet high, he says, with slender back legs, smallish back paws, a heavy head, a long tail with a blunt end, and irregular, black and white stripes on both body and tail.

The Emmaville sheep-killer was reported as attacking the head and neck of the sheep (as a big cat might). It was reported as eating the whole sheep, except for the skin. In one case, it ate four sheep in one night.

This great appetite would seem to distinguish it from

the dingo, Australia's wild dog, which does not consume nearly so much at one sitting.

The habit of completely eating its prey also would differentiate the Emmaville sheep-killer from the Tasmanian wolf (also called the Tasmanian tiger), a striped, meat-eating animal that lives on the island of Tasmania, south of Australia (and maybe rarely on Australia itself). The Tasmanian wolf is choosy and selects only some parts of its victim to dine upon. The Tasmanian wolf also has a canine, or doglike, head that no one would mistake for a cat's.

An Emmaville man suggested that the unknown sheep-destroyer might emit a rank odor, not noticeable to human beings, but objectionable to other animals. This might explain why dogs seem to locate it first, and why even a fearless dog recoils from entering scrub where the animal has been.

Ellis Troughton, in *Furred Animals of Australia,* wrote about the tiger-cat: "Although such an animal has been reported on several occasions, no specimen has ever reached any museum to verify the occurrence scientifically. There are often simple explanations for such reports, but the consistency of the accounts suggests the possibility of the presence of some large carnivorous marsupial of the dasyurid family (which includes the thylacine)." The thylacine is the Tasmanian wolf.

"In future, observers should make every effort to obtain both the skull and complete skin of a specimen and ensure the preservation by heavy salting before forwarding the remains to the local museum."

Mr. Troughton cautioned against accepting the animal as real until that final proof is in. "The failure of observers to obtain any parts of the hide, hair, or skull, casts much doubt over the reports of such an animal," he wrote.

But there is a chance that an unknown tiger-cat could well exist in the land down under. Already, in the 1960's, Australians have discovered a possum that zoologists believed extinct, and a new species of snake-sized earthworm no one even knew existed. There are still zoological surprises ahead in Australia.

THE YALE MONSTER

Men from Yale University, fishing in the Pacific off the coast of Peru, caught—sort of by mistake—a possible world's record monster. They landed a manta ray, the great flatfish of the open sea, that weighed over a ton and a half. It may have been the hugest manta ever taken.

The manta ray is a mystery monster in that not a great deal is known about it. The Bingham Oceanographic Laboratory at Yale, and Dan Merriman, its director, wanted to study the manta.

"We had fought a manta ray for four-and-one-half hours off Africa," Ed Migdalski of Yale told me, "so I knew what it was like to try and get one. It was terrible." The African ray got away. Off Cabo Blanco, Peru, Migdalski and the Yale team tried again.

The manta ray, *Manta birostris,* also called the devilfish, devil ray, or vampire bat, in much fiction about the ocean, is also named the sea bat. The ray grows up to 18 feet or more across, or from wing tip to wing tip (its flapping fins at each side are called wings). The manta ray is a fine swimmer—and one of its mysteries is why this is so. Unlike most rays, the manta does not laze on the bottom of the sea but, instead, spends most of its time swimming powerfully at or near the surface, as does the shark, to which it is related. Here's what's puzzling about how it can swim so well: To help propel three thousand pounds through the sea, the manta has only a small, ratlike tail. No other almost tailless creature manages to swim like this. When the manta swims over a diver, the great wings blot out the light. This is one of the spookiest experiences you can have on the bottom of the sea.

The manta is also one of the great high jumpers of the sea—and the world. Why this is so is another complete stumper.

Dan Merriman, who is one of America's great marine biologists and has never yet been caught in even a slight embellishment of a fish story, tells you: "When lying at the surface, they apparently give a powerful downsweep with their huge fins, and hurl themselves up in the air fifteen feet or more.

"Frequently they somersault, and then fall back into the water with a resounding crash and a splash as if the Empire State building had dropped into the sea.

"Again and again we saw these monsters do their aerial acrobatics, a magnificent display of power and a never-ending source of fascination, save when they jumped too close for comfort and our minds turned to what would happen if a ton-and-a-half manta fell on board ship." The Yale party used four fishing boats, none large.

"Some persons," Merriman explains, "say the mantas leap to get rid of parasites, or suckerfish, clinging to them, but we saw no parasites on them.

"You know, if I could jump like that, I'd do it all the time, just for the fun of it."

Looking back on the struggle to catch and land the huge manta, Ed Migdalski told me simply, "I never thought we'd do it." The gigantic ray, instead of just an ordinary-sized one, was obtained, he says, because "we just happened to get into a fine mess of them. We saw five or six that day.

"A Peruvian, with a harpoon," Migdalski went on, "was standing on the starboard side of the bow of our fishing boat. She was the *Suzanne V* under Captain Bill Fagen of Miami.

"I was on my knees behind the harpooner, holding onto a five-gallon drum. A hundred fathoms of quarter-inch manila rope was wound around the drum and attached to it on one end; the other end of the rope was attached to the harpoon.

"At about 3 P.M., the ray was spotted, to starboard, close alongside the bow. At 3:02 the harpoon was hurled into the middle of its back."

From then on, the ray provided the Yale men with a whole series of man-sized crises. Crisis No. 1 happened instantly—it was the first thing the manta did.

Migdalski expected the ray to swim away from the *Suzanne V*. Instead, the devilfish crossed the bow. The rope was jerked across the bow deck with such force the

Peruvian lad could have been injured or swept overboard.

Migdalski screamed at the boy to duck under the rope. He did, barely in time.

Crisis No. 2 came a split second later. The powerful ray hauled the five-gallon drum across the boat's deck. The drum could have crashed into and carried away the rail on the port side. Migdalski, with all his strength, heaved the drum from the starboard of the vessel over the port rail. It cleared by inches.

The ray sped across the Pacific. It churned a great white wake on the surface. The *Suzanne V* pursued.

"We followed the ray for miles," says Migdalski. "The rope paid out rapidly from the drum. There was a slight chop on the sea, but it was easy to keep the ray in sight —what with the drum and the huge white wake, and the spray. Finally, we caught up with the drum and took it aboard."

Crisis No. 3—an hours-long fight—began.

"The ray would stop," Migdalski says, "and we would pull in rope as vigorously as we could. We were really putting it to him. We had to exhaust his strength. We couldn't let him rest."

Crisis No. 4: The rope got all fouled up on deck. Anyone could have been caught in it and dragged overboard. "I kept an open knife right by my hand all the time, in case someone should get the rope around an arm or leg," Migdalski recalls.

"Sure, we had our procedure all planned, but this thing was so big. So big that things happened so we couldn't go according to plan."

When they got close enough, they shot the ray. "Bud

King, an angler on the expedition, was standing by. Bud hit him in what would have been vulnerable spots for any other animal. But he didn't kill him."

The *Suzanne V* drew alongside the giant fish. Crisis No. 5: When the ray was near the side of the boat, a huge wing would come flapping and crashing over the rail.

Everyone had to sidestep, hop, jump, or run to duck the blows that might have meant a nasty wound.

"Then," says Ed Migdalski, "we tried to gaff him." Crisis No. 6.

"We would get marlin gaffs—big iron hooks—into him and he would straighten them right out—as easily as you bend a paper clip. We lost five gaffs that way."

That was all the gaffs they had. Crisis No. 7: How could they bring in the devilfish without gaffs?

The flapping wing crashing over the side provided an idea.

"As the wing came over," says Migdalski, "we would grap it momentarily and hold onto it. I would gouge it with a knife. After many tries we got a hole in the wing.

"Then we got a rope through the hole, and tied the wing securely.

"Finally we got a rope around his body. No, I don't know how we did it, but we did. It took about an hour and a half to tie him up. Then we dragged him astern into the port of Cabo Blanco.

"As we entered, I looked at my watch. It was twenty minutes to eleven." Seven hours and thirty-eight minutes from the time the harpoon landed.

The ray died, in the harbor, that night.

Next day, the rope towing the manta was transferred from the *Suzanne V* to a motor launch. The launch hauled the ray to a pier.

Natives took over the rope in an effort to haul the ray ashore. Even after death, the giant fish caused trouble. Crisis No. 8: The Peruvians could pull the manta through the water all right, but not onto the beach.

Cabo Blanco's school kids were let out, and everyone, young and old, grabbed the rope and tried to pull the ray over the sand. No success.

Oil company trucks came along. The rope was attached to the rear axle of one. Men and truck pulled. Together, they got the ray up two feet on the beach.

Crisis No. 9: The truck looked as if it were about to fall apart. The truck detached, and departed.

Logs and lumber were put under the ray. Another truck plus men got him up ten or fifteen feet more. The second truck was forced to quit.

A third truck, with everyone in sight also pulling, finally got the ray well up the beach.

Then Migdalski, with native helpers, went to work pouring plaster for a plaster cast of the ray.

Crisis No. 10: The tide started coming in.

Migdalski realized it would roll over the ray, plaster and all.

"I was ready," he recalls, "to give up for the tenth time.

"But everybody got busy and built a dike of sand around the ray. The dike was three feet high, and completely surrounded the animal except where it met a high bank at the back. The day—and the ray—were saved."

Laboring under the broiling sun, which he had not felt during the chase, but did feel now, Migdalski took two-and-one-half days to make plaster molds of the ray. He got one break. Despite the sun, "the ray," he says, "didn't smell." The molds were so large they could not be loaded onto the *Suzanne V* or any of the U.S. fishing vessels in the vicinity, and had to be shipped to Yale aboard a freighter.

For the ray measured 18½ feet across—from wing tip to wing tip.

At 3,300 pounds, it was the heaviest ray ever weighed.

As the Yale ray was not put on the scales until it had been cut into pieces and therefore had lost some of its body fluid and had become dehydrated by being out of the water, it had probably been at least a couple of hundred pounds heavier when Migdalski & Company were fighting it.

I have found only one story of a manta ray that might have been as heavy, and might have been heavier than Yale's great catch. On February 14, 1919, the National Geographic Society *Book of Fishes* reports, Captain Charles H. Thompson and a fishing party in the Gulf Stream off Florida hauled in a big one. The ray was harpooned. Even with its life ebbing from the harpoon wound, it towed a twenty-five-foot motorboat ten miles. The ray's measurements: 22 feet across from the tip of one pectoral fin to the tip on the other side; 17 feet 1 inch from head to end of tail (a manta ray is almost as long as it is broad). It weighed, "considerably more than 3,000 pounds." It might even have weighed 4,000, but the scales they had would not go over 3,000, so they claimed no greater weight.

Captain Thompson's party was on board a yacht, *L'Apache,* owned by James A. Allison, and included

Captain Thompson of Miami, Commodore Charles W. Kotcher, A. G. Batchelder, John Oliver La Gorce, and Captain Paterson and the crew of the *L'Apache*.

At 3,300 pounds, the Yale manta ray was a lot heavier than record catches of some other big fishes. The record man-eating white shark taken on rod and reel, 2,664 pounds, was caught by Alfred Dean off South Australia in 1959. The record black marlin, caught by rod and reel, was 1,560 pounds in weight. It was caught August 4, 1953, by A. C. Glassell, Jr. Mr. Glassell caught his marlin off Cabo Blanco, Peru, where Yale caught the manta ray. The year before, 1952, the record for black marlin was broken four times in the Cabo Blanco area.

Yale caught its ray in April 1953. The Yale men looked in one of the most likely places in the world to find such a monster: Off Cabo Blanco, Peru, in the Humboldt Current, the life of the sea teems as it does almost nowhere else on earth. The ray was only one of a number of monsters the Yale men encountered. The sights seen by the members of the expedition are the kind they will tell their grandchildren about.

Jim Morrow, the chief scientist of the expedition, tried to harpoon a blackfish one day. There were so many blackfish around his boat, they ran into each other trying to get away. A blackfish is a small whale. Their presence was one evidence of the profusion of life in the Humboldt Current. The current, which runs north along the coasts of Chile and Peru, and then turns west across the Pacific, is the ocean stream that, fourteen years ago, pushed a raft called the *Kon-tiki* away from Peru and thereby started the raft on its now famous voyage across the ocean. "Nobody knows what is there," says Dan Merriman about the Humboldt Current. "You can't help adding to knowledge about it."

Sally Wheatland of the Yale party saw five sperm whales at one time, a rare sight in this time of small whale populations. A sight of one these days is enough to cause excitement. The sperm whale was, and is, one of the whales most hunted by whaling ships. Sharks abound in the Humboldt. There was the great whale shark, largest of all fishes, the shark that grows up to 60 feet long, and has jaws 5 feet wide with which it achieves a bulldog grin. There were five or six hammerheads a day. There were sand sharks.

One day the Yale party hooked a white shark. "This," says Jim Morrow, "is The man-eater with a capital *t*." It is rare to encounter a white shark. "We estimated it was 16 feet long and weighed 1,200 pounds," says Morrow. "We played it two hours, then it rolled up in the line and snapped it." Added Miss Wheatland, "The sight was enough to keep me from swimming the rest of the time."

There was at least one spinner shark—and he spun. Dan Merriman tells about it: "I saw three spinner sharks on one day, or maybe it was the same one jumping three times. I don't know which. These weigh a hundred pounds or more, jump out of the water, travel through the air a way, and then re-enter. As they sail through the air they revolve, end around end, head around tail, like a wheel spinning parallel to the water." The spinning shark, says Merriman, was the most brilliant performer of all the ocean beasts that were observed.

The air was as full of life as the water. This is from Merriman's diary: "Brown pelicans everywhere, in flight singly . . . or in hundreds, gorging on small silversides

... Peruvian cormorants, smaller than ours, *the* guano birds; blue-footed boobies; many frigate birds—wonderfully long tails; Mother Carey's chickens; gulls (not many) and royal terns." The sea lions of Peru and the birds are the harvesters who gather up the fish life of the Humboldt Current; that is, they get some of the fish not eaten up by each other. "The pelicans," says Merriman, "eat so much they can hardly get out of the water, and fly home a foot or two above the surface."

There were game fish too in the Humboldt Current. The Yale group landed 3 black marlin, 20 striped marlin, 14 sailfish, 4 tuna, 3 mako sharks, and hundreds of smaller fish: rooster fish, bonito, Spanish mackerel, blue runners, jacks, and dolphins.

Merriman himself, fishing from the fifty-foot *Mañana III*, hauled in a 10-foot, 126-pound sailfish, a good-sized catch but not a record. Scientist Merriman wanted to dissect his catch so that he could learn every blessed thing about it. The boat's skipper, Bill Lance, was so shocked by this unfishermanlike behavior that he rushed to his radio mike and spluttered the unbelievable news across the Pacific:

"He's the first angler I ever saw who started to cut up his fish before he had his picture taken."

Wendell W. Anderson, Yale '22, a Detroit manufacturer who sponsored the expedition, landed a 797-pound black marlin, the biggest game-fish catch. Mrs. Anderson brought in a 337-pound big-eye tuna, a women's world's record and a world's record for both men and women on twenty-four-thread tackle.

Jim Morrow brought in one of those plentiful dolphins, and, like Merriman, he paid scientific attention to what he was doing. The dolphin—Morrow caught the fish, not the porpoise of the same name—is famous for changing colors. Morrow carefully noted the details: "My dolphin jumped five times," he says. "It was each of the following colors on one jump: green, blue, yellow, orange, and purple. This is because of a nervous reaction that causes color change because of contraction of the pigment cells."

The dolphins are not the only fish to add color to the Humboldt Current. Luminescent deep-sea fish rise toward the surface at night, sometimes reach it, and sometimes dot the Humboldt with red and green eyes, or stripe the current's surface with glowing streaks. Working between 10 P.M. and 2 A.M., the Yale scientists went after deep-sea fish. "They were," Merriman says, "a never-ending source of fascination because of their peculiar modifications." Most were black, and most had light organs. Samples pulled in included the myctophid, a fish with light organs running along its side like a row of portholes on a ship; and the *Chauliodus,* six inches long, equipped with long, thin fangs whose function seems to be to hold littler fish in its mouth, as in a cage, till it can swallow them.

Even a single bucketful of fish could teem with excitement. "We came up," says Miss Wheatland, of one trawl, "with a number of deep-sea fish—red shrimp, salps, jellyfish, etc. We were greatly pleased.

"But the skipper, looking at our catch, which would have fit easily into a bucket, announced once again that he thought all scientists were crazy."

Some of the fish in the Humboldt even throw themselves at you. The squid, creatures like octopuses except that squid have ten arms while the octopus has eight, can leap through the air. This they manage by a kind of jet propulsion. Squid, that is, hurl themselves by expelling sea water, a previously known fact the Yale party observed. "They would jump right into the boat," says Miss Wheatland. "Sometimes they would hit you right in the eye."

From the sea, the Yale people watched white-capped mountains turn black with life. Dan Merriman explains. "It isn't unusual to look in from the sea and see snow-covered mountains. When you look at Peru's famous guano islands, they too are white. But when the birds come in, the summits change to solid black—and so, too, do the whole islands."

Jim Morrow, speaking of the guano birds, says: "One evening, near the guano islands, we saw a flock of birds coming back. The flock was a quarter of a mile wide, ten or twelve feet above the water, and you couldn't see the end of the flock. It was past the horizon, over ten miles away that day." The sea itself changed color, Gerald Posner, the party's oceanographer, explained: It became bright red from the sudden blooming of tiny plant organisms called dinoflagellates.

Summarizing the profusion of fish life in the Humboldt, Dan Merriman said: "One morning we saw birds working over the sea—thousands of them. Those birds had come to feed on anchovy-sized fish. The anchovetas were chased by jacks. The jacks circled so the tiny fish were close together. You could see the jacks snapping up their meal.

"There wasn't any water there. You could have got out and walked on the fish." It is, he said, impossible to exaggerate the life in the Humboldt. It is small wonder that Yale found a giant manta ray right there.

Ed Migdalski caught another record-breaking fish on the same trip when the manta ray was obtained. It was a 148-pound, 4-foot-4-inch *Arapaima gigas.* Migdalski's was the first arapaima known to be caught by a man in almost forty years. It is one of the world's biggest freshwater fishes. It lives only in remote places like western equatorial Africa, Australia, Indonesia, and eastern South America where, in British Guiana, Migdalski landed his. Migdalski used a twelve-to-fifteen-pound line. That meant his arapaima was the largest fish ever taken on such light tackle. The arapaima is a distant relative of the herring, salmon, tarpon, and trout. Its long, cylindrical body is covered with olive-green scales that, halfway back to the tail, begin having red edges.

Migdalski also caught many piranhas, the flesh-eating fish of South American rivers; a twenty-seven-pound, black, orange, and white catfish; and an electric eel. When I asked him to comment on his fisherman's luck, Migdalski said: "I'd rather fish than eat. I love to eat 'em. I love to work with them. I feel I am more closely related to fish than to most people."

On the wall of Ed Migdalski's office at Yale, there hangs the famous Fisherman's prayer:

<blockquote>
Oh Lord!
Let me catch a fish
so darn big
that when I tell about it
I won't have to lie.
</blockquote>

Migdalski, who has "been fishing ever since I can remember; since I could walk, I guess," never will have to exaggerate about his ray. "I will tell the story," he told me "the rest of my days."

The funny thing about the whole story was that Migdalski wasn't out after the biggest ray, didn't want it, in fact. An average-sized ray might have been more useful scientifically.

Migdalski wanted a manta small enough so it could be caught, hauled in, and plaster-cast with a reasonable amount of work.

But since the afternoon was getting along—it was, you remember three o'clock when the monster ray was sighted—Expedition Leader Wendell Anderson told Migdalski he'd better attack this ray or he wouldn't get any.

That was why, although the party had spotted five or six rays that same afternoon, Migdalski went after this one, but hadn't chased any of the others.

"I thought they were too big," he says, "and turned them down."

FOUND ALIVE--
AFTER 1200 YEARS!

When he opened a door that had been shut longer than almost any door in the Americas, a young U. S. scientist named Joseph R. Valenta caught up with some of the littlest, oldest, most mysterious monsters in the world.

The door had been closed, for the last time before Valenta opened it, twelve hundred years ago—or seven hundred years *before* Columbus discovered America.

What Valenta found were bacteria. They had survived —individuals had lived—for those twelve hundred years. How they did it is a puzzle that science is trying to solve.

Valenta is a doctor. He is also a microbiologist—he studies small animals through microscopes. He had traveled deep into the jungle in Guatemala, Central America, to make his discovery, to a place called Tikal.

At Tikal there is an ancient Mayan temple. Beneath the temple, sealed shut, there is an underground, 12-by-18-foot tomb. From the tomb Dr. Valenta got one of the most surprising items ever obtained from any tomb anywhere: individual animals that have survived far longer, so far as we know, than any other living thing—ever.

The tomb Dr. Valenta entered was closed up not long after the fall of the Roman Empire. That's when the bacteria must have got into it.

Yet they are alive today.

On November 7, 1962, Dr. Valenta and Aubrey S. Trik, an archeologist of the University of Pennsylvania, became the first to enter the tomb since it had been sealed, back in the Middle Ages.

The entrance was covered by a capstone, a five hundred-pound block of limestone. The stone was removed by a heavy-duty chain hoist. As soon as it was removed, a sheet of clear plastic was placed over the opening. The plastic was to prevent bacteria from today's world from entering the tomb and getting mixed with any others that might be inside. Dr. Valenta, of course, had no way of knowing what he would find in the tomb.

He crawled down a ladder—a 2-by-5-inch piece of lumber with iron spikes as rungs.

When he came to the bottom of the tomb, Dr. Valenta was surrounded by dust and debris. This did not bother him in the least; it was where the bacteria, if any, would be, the dust and debris were what he had come to collect.

He wanted to keep the dust and debris uninfected by any germs he himself might bring, so he wore sterile garments, he had a mask over his mouth, and he had sterilized his digging instruments. With these instruments,

Can an animal live over a thousand years? In Philadelphia, Dr. Joseph R. Valenta studies bacteria he brought back from Tikal, Guatemala, and revived after what apparently was one of longest sleeps on record.

he gathered powdered wood, plaster scrappings, volcanic chips, mortar, charcoal, and bits of limestone.

This, probably one of the most important shipments of dust and debris ever made, was flown back to Philadelphia.

There, in the Smith Kline & French Laboratories, Dr. Valenta put some of his samples onto plates that duplicated the temperature and humidity outside the tomb in the Guatemalan jungle—i.e., the sort of world the bacteria must have lived in originally.

Home of what may be the longest-lived animals yet discovered was this Mayan tomb at Tikal, Guatemala. Men in photo helped open the tomb—which had been sealed, with bacteria inside, for over a millennium.

Would there be anything alive now?
There was.
Within forty-eight hours, Dr. Valenta observed growth on several of the plates.

The bacteria, dormant all those centuries, still lived.

This was only the beginning of the studies that Dr. Valenta and other scientists are making of the bacteria. The Mayan civilization, Dr. Valenta knows, vanished for no known reason. Are these bacteria the cause? Are they disease-bearing? And, if so, did they bring down the Mayas?

Are they the same as known bacteria today, or do they represent a biological form that no longer exists? Are they relatives or ancestors of today's germs? Will they help us develop new medicines? Dr. Valenta has isolated a type of bacteria, from among his ancient ones, that he thinks may lead to new antibiotics.

The bacteria from the tomb at Tikal are, by far, the longest-lived animals on earth. No known animal even competes with the Tikal bacteria for living a long time. Among the oldest of other creatures in the world are Galapagos tortoises that are believed to have reached 200 to 250 years, or one-sixth as old as Dr. Valenta's little monsters. A Russian sturgeon was credited with living 200 to 300 years. A sea anemone may live to be 100, a whale, 37 to 40 years. Bears, which sleep deeply over the winter, but do not lie dormant for centuries as did the Tikal bacteria, live 30 to 34 years. A condor has been known to live 52 years; a starling, 17; and an English sparrow, 23. The European catfish, or wels, has been observed to live 60 years; the European eel, 40. An alligator may live 56 years, and an elephant, in spite of exaggerated legends about its longevity, no more than 70. A Labrador dog named Adjutant died in Revesby, England, in November 1963, at 27 years of age. It was believed to be the oldest dog in the world.

The shortest-lived vertebrate animal—animal with a backbone—is the goby, a fish that may be swimming in a bowl in your front room. The goby is born, grows up, lives, and dies in less than a year.

Men today are thinking about traveling to the moon. After that, they may attempt trips to other planets. Some planets are so far away from the earth that, even at the speeds of spaceships, they will take longer to reach than men are likely to live. Therefore, a way for men to hibernate, or lie dormant, as Dr. Valenta's bacteria did, might enable men to live long enough to get to a faraway planet.

How to suspend life processes during years-long interplanetary journeys is one of the most important subjects that the Guatemalan bacteria just might shed light on, that is, the biggest mystery about them is simply the most startling thing about them, after all: How in this world can anything remain alive—after twelve hundred years?

"IT HAS THE DEATH RAY"

The baggage clerk asked himself a common question: "Is the electric eel really electric?" He thought that, to find out, he'd touch the eel in the long wooden shipping box.

He touched it.

The shock hurled him backwards across the car. Only the closed doors kept him aboard the train.

The electricity is real all right. "The electric eel," says Christopher Coates, until recently director of New York City Aquarium at Coney Island, "is the only animal in the world that can kill you without touching you.

"It has the death ray."

The electric eel was an entirely unknown animal till four hundred years ago. Spanish invaders of South America then came upon it. Many people, like the baggage clerk, wonder about it even yet.

So much remains unknown about the electric eel, in fact, that it is still a mystery monster. How does its death ray work? What are the eel's secrets? Mr. Coates is the first person in history to study scientifically and painstakingly the electric eel and its death ray. He has given over half his lifetime to it. For centuries after the eel had become known, it was overlooked. Coates was the first man to make himself thoroughly acquainted with it. Doing so, he demonstrated that a mystery monster had a whole wealth of scientific information of use to mankind. And from the amazing results of Coates' research, you can understand why a mystery monster may add a lot to mankind's knowledge.

The electric eel already has.

Yet it poses so many riddles that it will take many scientists many years to find the answers.

Back in 1929, Christopher William Coates, then a youth, draped himself over a rail of the old New York Aquarium, at the Battery, and watched one of the few electric eels then in the U.S. swim around. He noted, and was not convinced by, the sign, behind the tank, that said the eel could discharge enough juice to knock down a horse. "I was dubious," Coates admits.

He determined to find out. By 1932 he had got himself on the aquarium payroll in charge of tropical fish—one of which is the electric eel. No one then knew much about the eel. Alexander von Humboldt, the nineteenth-century explorer of South America, had regarded the electric eel as so much of a mystery that he explained in detail to his readers what happened when he stepped on one with both feet. "I was," Humboldt reported, "affected during

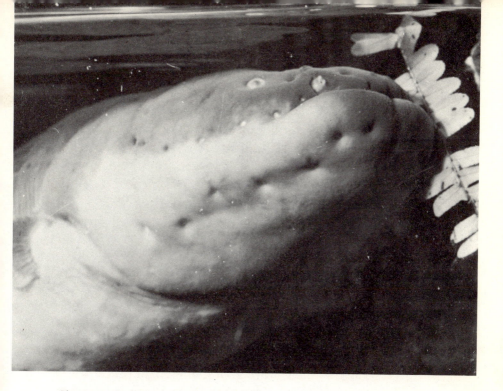

Close-up of electric eel shows pits that receive radar signals that locate its prey. "Nothing I have ever learned about this incredible creature," says Dr. Christopher Coates, "has astounded me more."

the rest of the day with a violent pain in the knees and in every joint."

Another explorer in South America, Up de Graff, knew so little about the eel that he attempted to cut off its head with a machete, the great steel knife of the tropics. He recovered, but, he said, "I might just as well have tried to cut a trolley wire with uninsulated pliers. The machete flew out of my hand and my arm was temporarily paralyzed."

Coates, in his first experiments, got together a lot of paraphernalia—mainly wires and lamps—and tried to trap the eel's current and to get it to light an incandescent bulb. One of the first things that happened was that he felt the shock the railway clerk and Humboldt and Up de Graff had felt. He tried to pick up an eel. The animal picked him up instead, knocked him off his feet.

"Once you've felt it," says Coates, "you'll swear to the power of the electric eel. At least, I guarantee you'll swear."

A year of work got no results. The light bulb never showed the slightest sign of glowing.

The turning point in Coates's experiments, and the turning point in the story of the electric eel to date, came one Saturday afternoon when Coates was hot, tired, and discouraged. His eels were giving him a bad time. "I was," he says, "being given a demonstration of the Harvard law of animal behavior: that animals under the most exactly controlled conditions do exactly as they please."

An eel pleased to shock him into jumping into the air. But at the same time Coates thought he saw a neon pip, now connected in place of the incandescent bulb, emit a glow. Coates wasn't sure whether he had seen a real glow—or stars from the shock. He tried again. He saw another orange glow.

A neon pip looks like a small electric bulb. Inside the glass, though, there is a metal part that looks like a radio tube. With its gentle glow, the pip is widely used as a night light. Coates knew at once why it had lit: The pip responds instantaneously, whereas the incandescent bulb, which failed to light, needs a warm-up period of one fiftieth of a second. The eel's discharge does not last long enough to turn on an incandescent bulb.

"I also knew," says Coates, "that the eel's potential was at least eighty volts, because that was the minimum necessary to light the neon pip."

The lighting of the neon pip was a turning point also because it proved for the first time (1) that the eel discharged real electricity, and (2) that something could be done with it.

From then on Coates did a great deal with it: He hooked up an eel to take its own picture by setting off a photoflash. At New York City's Bronx Zoo, he made some eels power a sign, ELECTRIC EEL. He had one start the engines on a New York City fireboat. He made one turn on a searchlight atop the sixty-story Woolworth building.

When we visted him at Coney Island, Coates put on for my wife, Janie, and me a demonstration exactly like the one you can see any time you visit the aquarium. He stood behind a glass tank containing three eels. He stroked beneath their chins with a rod. They discharged. A loudspeaker crackled. Neon lights swiftly glowed, faded. Jagged green flashes danced across the screen of an oscillograph.

But most impressive was the voltometer, a tall gadget looking like a thermometer, that measures the voltage an eel is putting out. Once it flashed 525 as we watched. Most often it was around 350. From a 6-foot, 80-pound eel, thick as a man's thigh, Coates has noted 625 volts, the most yet.

Cavendish, Sir Humphry Davy, Michael Faraday, and Benjamin Franklin all had known of the electric eel—

and sometimes dabbled with it. But Coates was the first man to demonstrate its voltage.

Coates has also shown more about eel electricity: Though high in voltage, it is low in amperage (usually a fraction of an amp, it reaches up to one ampere), and of short duration. One discharge lasts only one five-hundredth of a second, which is why it didn't light the incandescent bulb.

It is interrupted direct current. Its death ray is composed of killing bolts, hurled out by the eel in groups of ten, like bursts of ten machine-gun shots, never one at a time. An eel can discharge 40 of these bursts a second, 400 bolts of lightning altogether. At one five-hundredth of a second per discharge, this means the eel is discharging electricity in an almost continuous series of pulses.

The eel cannot keep up at this rate. It can, however, get off 1,600 discharges in the first five seconds, and, even when tired, can still hurl its lightning 100 or 150 times a second. The eel's power never weakens—only the number of discharges is reduced. Why this is so no one knows—it is one of the mysteries about the eel. Even after the eel has been discharging for twenty minutes, a five-minute rest is all it needs to recharge its batteries, get back to normal, and start operating again at full capacity.

The electric eel is the only animal that discharges electricity in order to obtain prey. Three other fishes do produce electricity enough to shock, but only to drive away, their enemies: Nile catfishes, torpedoes, and stargazers. Weak electricity is produced also by skates, mormyrids, and lampreys. In producing a strong current for meal-gathering, and for defense and offense as well

—in possessing the death ray—the electric eel is unique in the animal kingdom.

To carry on his detailed research, Coates had to become the first man to import into the U.S. electric eels in large numbers. The New York Aquarium is today the center of supply for universities and other aquariums. "We've had fifteen to twenty thousand pass through here," Coates estimates.

Coates imports his eels from only one source, the only place they live. That's the South American river systems of the Amazon and Orinoco. These river systems are connected to each other. The luxuriant river jungle (trees to 200 feet tall) is full of creatures almost as surprising as the eel: the world's largest rodent—the 4½-foot-long capybara; anteaters 6 feet long; jaguars larger than leopards; the giant armadillo; the tapir, a 300-pound, elephantlike, prehistoric animal; the world's biggest ant, the alligator ant, 1¼ inches in length; the world's largest beetle—6 inches long; centipedes, scorpions, ticks, red bugs, and great spiders, and blood-sucking bats. A young naturalist named Charles Darwin was the first to prove South America's vampire bats were real, when he saw one sucking the blood of a horse. Birds include vultures, toucans (with bills as long as their bodies), and parakeets more common than sparrows.

In the waters with the eel are the manatee, or sea cow; the anaconda, probably the largest serpent on the globe; crocodiles; innumerable kinds of frogs and toads; and perhaps eighteen hundred species of fish. The fish include some relatives of the eel: a great catfish and the flesh-eating piranha and the tiny one-inch-long neon tetra that glows like an electric sign and comes up from South

America to inhabit many tropical-fish bowls in U.S. homes.

They are relatives of the eel, as is also the carp. The electric eel is no eel at all, but a fish. It is not at all related to the common, moray, or conger, eels. Only its snakelike shape is similar.

In regions as strange as the Amazon and Orinoco basins, you might expect to find something as queer as a fish you can drown, and you do: the electric eel. It must breathe air, every four minutes, and it comes to the surface to do so. (Two other fishes that can be drowned are the lungfish and, believe it or not, the tarpon.)

Apparently all the fish and animals of the jungle respect the electric eel. Of the thousands of eels Coates has handled, only three have had their tails chewed up, indicating that something attacked them. Specimens of other fishes are constantly getting bitten. There is no known animal that is the natural enemy of the eel. However, leeches, smaller than a child's fingernail, can anchor through the gluey slime that covers an eel and fasten onto the skin. More than 2,375 leeches were removed from a two-foot eel. Possibly the leech is so simply constructed it is immune to electrical shock.

But eels do fight each other. One grabs another with its almost toothless gums. A fatal electrical burn may thus be inflicted. But the bitten eel will never die till the next day—why, is another mystery to science.

The eel does not electrocute itself because its tissue is rectified, that is, it passes the current only one way. No other animal flesh is rectified. The eel cannot live in salt water. In salt water it is short-circuited and it literally discharges itself to death. The same thing happens if an eel is laid on a sheet of aluminum.

Like the railway baggage clerk who touched the eel to see what would happen, at least two animals are known to have contacted the electric eel to their sorrow. Into the New York Aquarium, Coates once brought a large tomcat to keep down rats. Old Tom did all right till he decided a fish diet was better. He consumed some of the aquarium's choicest specimens (fish at $200 or so a pound). Then one night he went for a small electric eel.

Aquarium men the next morning detected what had happened from splashes around the eel's tank and scratches on the eel. They found Old Tom huddled in the most remote coalbin in the place. Old Tom never had a taste for fish after that.

And a dog was once seen to try to make friends with an eel. He licked it. The pup gyrated around in the air for a few seconds. He never went near an eel again.

Much of the Amazon-Orinoco jungle is low, swampy, often flooded; and here the electric eel hides a secret from Coates and all other scientists. It goes off into the swamps to raise a family. No one knows how—whether by laying eggs, giving birth to live young, or what. Afterwards, a parent eel will return to the river, with fifty to one hundred or more young ones, an inch long, swimming about its head. The babies can shock. They make your fingers tingle.

Having grown up to about six inches long and three hundred volts, a young eel leaves its father—or mother. You cannot tell Dad from Mom. From then on, its life is one of ease that a man lolling in the Miami sun might well envy. The brown, dark green, or black eel stays down in the mud in shallow water (except for breathing) and loafs, or swims slowly. It never chases dinner because, with its death ray, it has no need to, and at the most it swims lazily till a meal happens by. It first locates a meal by means of weak electric discharges that work something like radar or sonar.

"It sends out," says Coates, "frequent electric impulses, which, striking fish or frogs or worms, or anything else, bounce back." These small discharges go out twenty or thirty times a second while the eel is just mozeying around. They are discharged from the rear of the eel's tail, where they are produced.

No one knew how the eels received back their messages until Coates, curious about some small pits arranged around the eel's head, painted over the pits with lacquer. The eels so treated could find no food. The pits are its receiving apparatus. Traveling at the speed of light from tail to prey and back to the pits in an eel's head, the waves exactly locate for the eel its next meal. The eel is never confused by its own movement, that of its prospective victim, or reflections from such things as the sides of a tank or the banks of a river.

"Nothing I have ever learned about this incredible creature," says Coates, "has astounded me more."

Once it locates something, the eel, with a twitch of its spine, hurls out its death ray—its series of heavy killing or paralyzing discharges. Entirely voluntary on the part of the eel, these discharges are probably the fastest movement found in any animal. They are twelve to fifteen times as fast as an impulse traveling along one of your own nerves.

These invisible bolts of lightning kill or stun a fish or frog or even a man or large animal up to many feet away. Then the eel approaches its victim and nuzzles it. If it is too big—a man or a cow is because of the eel's toothless jaws—the eel moves away and leaves it. The victim, if he hasn't drowned, may recover in a few minutes. If the prey is small enough, the eel swallows its dinner whole. This makes the eel's cheeks puff out like balloons. Only that's the stomach, located where your cheeks are.

The front one fifth of the eel's long body, in fact, contains all its necessary organs. The complete animal, except for its power plant, is in the front 15 inches of a 6-foot-long eel: mouth; stomach; intestines; anal hole (a vent beneath the flat chin); two tiny eyes, often cloudy and almost blind—because of cataracts, possibly due to exposure to electricity.

Beneath the chin there is a splotch of color. As you might expect from where it is located, this seems to be the eel's Old School Tie. In other words, the color indicates what river it's from—red or reddish brown for the Amazon, yellow for the Orinoco. On each side of the head are two small, curved fins, almost rabbit ears.

The eel swims in its lazy, wavy motion by means of a single, long scalloped fin running along where a boat has its keel. The eel uses the same fin to go backwards just as easily as forwards, or to climb or move downward in the water.

South American Indians collect the eels for Coates. "They don't like to," he says. "They have the best possible reason: They are afraid of them." They know what the eels can do. An Indian boy, swimming, received the full shock of the eel. He was hauled ashore unconscious, but was resuscitated. Coates protects the Indians as well as he can. He sends them rubber gloves and aprons just like his own. The Indians either net the eels or spear them with wooden harpoons. This is one of the few cases where a man harpoons an animal he plans to sell alive. It does no serious harm if the harpoon enters the muscles or the eel's electric tissue, which makes his juice. The electric tissue, in fact, regenerates itself so you'd never know it had been damaged.

The rear four fifths of the eel, its long, streamlined tail, which the Indians try to spear, is mostly electric tissue. "This electric tissue," says Coates, "is a very special kind of flesh." The tissue is broken down into thousands of small pieces, equivalent to cells in a storage battery, that are separated by thin walls of electrically resistant flesh. The cells are the actual producers of electricity. Each cell creates about one tenth of a volt. By hooking up these tiny batteries together in series, so to speak, the eel builds up its powerful discharge. By chemical means, the animal throws on and off thousands of switches in its nervous system, and so turns on and off its juice. Somehow, by methods not understood (another mystery), all of the eel's cells discharge at almost exactly the same instant. This gives the eel its fullest possible power for use in attacking.

I looked at a piece of the electric tissue. White, it looks very much like an uncooked scallop. It felt flabbier, like very thick jello. When you hold it in your fingers, it seems to quiver.

The river Indians once used captive electric eels for shock treatment for sick persons. White men pooh-poohed the idea. Another native tale was that eating electric eel would cure rheumatism. A white doctor tried it and said he'd prefer rheumatism.

Nevertheless, American medical men, aided by Coates, have taken up the study of the electric eel with a vengeance—and with eye-opening results.

Coates sends electric eels—carried in plastic bags in cardboard boxes on subway trains—up to researchers at Columbia University's College of Physicians and Surgeons. Along with the electric tissue in its long tail, the eel has two hundred big, coarse nerves. They are much easier to study than the far smaller nerves of other animals and of men, which they resemble. Scientists learned from the electric eel's system how nerve gas kills a man.

What happens is that nerve gas, by blocking out the functioning of your nerves, can kill you in minutes. The gas can be carried in missiles, and could wipe out much of a city's population. Gas masks work against them only sometimes.

Today, after years of work under Dr. David Nachmansohn and Dr. Irvin B. Wilson, at Columbia University, there is a certain antidote, PAM, for nerve gas. This amounts to a victory in the cold war; it neutralizes nerve gas possessed by any prospective enemy. The electric eel has helped keep the peace.

But the successful development of an antidote for one of modern war's most dreadful weapons may be only the beginning of the eel's service to mankind. Those big nerves, it turns out, are so nearly a large mock-up of human nerves that today the electric eel is under observation and experimentation for facts that may help eliminate

Parkinson's disease, epilepsy, and other nervous disorders. Furthermore, the nervous system of the electric eel may shed light on how you see, hear, feel, taste, smell, move, and think.

In addition to all this, the National Inventors Council, a clearinghouse of ideas for the military services, recently said that one of its most-wanted inventions was a man-made generator on the order of the electric eel. One use for it would be to power repeater amplifiers in undersea cables.

"The electric eel," says Coates, "is the most important research animal there is, at this moment." For a mystery monster that was an all-but-unknown stick-in-the-mud till Christopher Coates went to work on it, the electric eel has come a long way.

THE POSSUM THAT PLAYED DEAD 50 YEARS

H. E. Wilkinson, a trained and experienced Australian zoologist, made a major biological discovery and ended a fifty-year-old mystery when he found a squirrel-sized animal—Leadbeater's possum—that was believed to be extinct. He did it in about the most unlikely way you can imagine. He came across the creature in the dark. And when he solved one mystery, Wilkinson set up another the biologists will talk about for years. He found the possum on land many times burned over. "What stumps me," David Fleay wrote in *The National Geographic Magazine*, "is that the long-lost animal was found in an area that time and time again has been ravaged by frightful bush fires. How has such a small creature of limited mobility managed to survive in such a region? I do not know the answer."

Believed extinct, and unseen for 50 years, Leadbeater's possum was discovered again recently. Distinguishing feature: its long, bushy tail. That gave it away. Possum is much like sugar glider (see next photo).

Mr. Wilkinson not only encountered the animal when there was little light to see by, but he also was handicapped by the fact that he only got a good look at one part of the creature. The part he could see was the tail, "a long, thin tail," he says, "bushing out towards the tip."

"I suddenly realized," he recalls, "that it was probably a Leadbeater's possum."

That was in 1961.

Leadbeater's possum, a brown or gray (and hard-to-see-in-the-dark) animal, was (and is) one of the rarest animals in the world. In 1961, it was known from only five mounted specimens in the National Museum in the state of Victoria, Australia. The last of the five specimens had been received at the museum in 1909.

The possum had been discovered first less than one hundred years ago. It was found in July 1867, in the Bass River valley of South Gippsland, Australia. The exact location is not known. The place is described as "the scrub on the banks of the Bass River in Victoria." This locality is one where you might expect an unknown possum: It harbors other strange animals. It is home to the egg-laying, fur-bearing platypus, the mammal with the duck's bill. It is home to giant earthworms many feet long that can tunnel through the ground faster than you can dig them out, and that you have to tie in knots to capture.

A professor, Frederick McCoy, named the possum *Gymnobelideus leadbeateri*. McCoy, around 1870, was working from the two specimens then known. Not till 1900 did another turn up. It was found, mounted, by Sir Baldwin Spencer, in a dealer's shop. Another Leadbeater's possum turned up in an accountant's office. When the fifth specimen reached the Victoria museum in 1909, no one recognized what it was. By 1921, the possum was regarded as extinct. But over the years, Australia's zoologists continued to watch for it. They did not find it and, in 1960, Leadbeater's possum was placed on a list of marsupials (animals that carry their young in a pouch) "extinct or almost extinct."

The next year Mr. Wilkinson found it—very much alive.

Wilkinson had begun a survey of mammals in the Mount Wills area. On April 3, 1961, he was in the Cumberland Valley, eleven miles east of Marysville, Victoria. He was not out in the wilderness. He was only seventy miles from the big city of Melbourne.

An hour after dark, he saw a small, gray creature. It was low down on the trunk of a blackwood tree. "It turned," he says, "and climbed quickly into the upper foliage, hesitated for a while, then jumped across to a neighboring tree and disappeared from view. When first seen it was thought to be a sugar glider (*Petaurus breviceps*)."

The sugar glider, a member of the possum family, is about the same size as Leadbeater's possum. It has membranes that let it glide 100 to 150 feet from the treetops.

Then Wilkinson saw the tail.

It wasn't the broad, fluffy tail of the sugar glider. It was that long, thin tail. It spread out towards the tip.

"Although," he says, "the tail was the only diagnostic feature seen clearly, it was enough to suggest a very exciting possibility, one which I had very much in mind while on the way to Marysville some three hours later."

Sugar glider is much like Leadbeater's possum (see previous photo). Sugar glider, another Australian possum, gets its name because it likes honey and because it sails 100 to 150 feet from treetops.

Wilkinson at this point was about to repeat one of the most amazing experiences in recent zoology. Having once come across an animal, unseen for over fifty years, in the dark, he was about to repeat the process, and encounter it again, still in the dark.

A nightjar flew in front of his car and perched by the side of the road.

To get a better look at the bird, he parked.

The nightjar flew off.

This did not matter in the least. He got a look instead at something that interested him more.

There, reflecting the beam of the spotlight of his car, were the two eyes of a very small possum.

It looked like—it looked a lot like—the creature he'd seen earlier that evening.

This time he could see more than the tail. He had ten minutes to watch.

The possum was brownish gray. It had no gliding membrane. So it definitely was not the sugar glider.

"Its size, build, and marking," he says, "readily distinguished it from any other small mammals with which it could possibly have been confused, and it seemed very probable that these two animals were indeed the long-lost Leadbeater's possum."

Excitedly, Wilkinson was back in the area five days later, after photographs. He got them.

He saw three Leadbeater's possums. He continued to follow his pattern—the first one he saw this time he found in the dark.

It was descending a mountain ash. "When about fifteen feet from the gound," Wilkinson wrote, in a publication of the Victoria museum, "it jumped to a sapling about

Willy the wombat, here aboard ship, is a strange Australian animal that recently reached New York's Bronx Zoo. Wombat has only two teeth—one upper, one lower—that it uses to bite roots.

five feet away, and quickly disappeared from view. Three hours later, and over a quarter of a mile away, two more were seen in silver wattle. One disappeared within a few seconds, but the other jumped to a mountain-ash limb and 'froze.' It was kept under observation for about twenty-five minutes, and several color photographs were taken of it."

They were the first pictures ever made of a living Leadbeater's possum.

Wilkinson had stayed on the trail of the animal in the first place because that long, spreading-out tail had been easy to recognize. The tail, 7 to 8 inches long, is longer than the possum's body, which is 5 to 6 inches.

The opossum of the U.S., with a 20-inch-long body and a naked tail a foot long is a larger animal. It keeps on living from New York to Florida, and from the Great Lakes to Texas, because, like Leadbeater's possum, the opossum is nocturnal—and thus keeps away from enemies like great horned owls, foxes, wolves, wildcats, dogs, and men. During the day it sleeps in a hollow tree or log.

The opossum is the only U.S. marsupial—the only American animal whose young are born undeveloped and then carried in a pouch as are the young of many Australian animals. When frightened, the opossum has the remarkable ability to feign death, or, as we say, to play possum. The name of the American animal is opossum; the Australian animal is a possum—no *o*.

As is sometimes the case with mystery animals, once Leadbeater's possum was identified, others promptly turned up.

Fifteen more Leadbeater's possums were spotted pretty quickly after Wilkinson first saw the animal. A specimen was sent to the Victoria museum. Several live possums were caught. The animal that had been unseen for half a century has settled down to captivity at Victoria's Fisheries and Wild Life Department. At last reports, it was doing very well.

THE SOAY BEAST

Not long ago when James Gavin, an engineer from London, was on vacation, he had the most unusual day of his lifetime. So did Tex Geddes, the professional fisherman who was his only companion. The two men spent over an hour of that day face to face with a huge, unknown monster.

Nobody knows what the monster was. It looked to both men something like a giant turtle, a turtle the size of an elephant. It swam toward them, across a stretch of the Sea of the Hebrides, for all the world like one of the big turtles that lived in the oceans in prehistoric times.

"Petrified, we watched it," Tex Geddes said, "as it came closer and closer."

"The head," said James Gavin, "was rather like that of a tortoise with a snakelike flattened cranium running

A great turtle may be mystery sea beast of Soay, Scotland. The 300-to-500-pound green turtle, shown on Ascension Island after nesting, actually crosses Atlantic to Brazil. National Science Foundation.

forward to a rounded face. Relatively it was as big as the head of a donkey."

"The head," said Geddes, "was definitely reptilian, about 2 feet 6 inches high, with large protruding eyes. . . . There were no visible nasal organs, but a large red gash of a mouth which seemed to cut the head in half and which appeared to have two distinct lips."

"I saw," said Gavin, "one laterally placed eye, round and large as that of a cow.

"When the mouth was opened I got the impression of

large blubbery lips and could see a number of tendril-like growths hanging from the palate."

The day James Gavin and Tex Geddes will never forget was Sunday, September 13, 1959. Gavin was spending his vacation in the Inner Hebrides islands, off the western coast of Scotland. It was a hot, clear day of sparkling visibility. You could see a long way.

It was just the sort of day that Gavin was looking for. It did not take him long, after he got an eye open that morning, to roll out of bed, gather his fishing gear, and get down to some rocks by the seaside. His intention was to spend the sunny day there, relaxing, resting, and fishing.

That was what he thought.

Gavin had scarcely settled down when Geddes appeared. Geddes was rowing a dinghy. Geddes said that the fishing might be better offshore and, generously, he invited Gavin to jump into the dinghy and come along.

Gavin accepted the hospitality. He hopped in.

Tex Geddes didn't know that he was rowing Gavin and himself right into the adventure of a lifetime. But he was. The men spent the day, entirely unexpectedly, in the company of three of the world's great monsters— one of them to this day an entirely unknown one.

In the case of Gavin, a landsman, unfamiliar with sea animals, this was not surprising.

In the case of Geddes, a professional fisherman of the Hebrides islands, a man thoroughly familiar with the sea creatures of the area, it was startling.

In the course of time, the experiences of Geddes and Gavin were published in *The Illustrated London News,* London's famous weekly picture magazine.

The Soay beast—as it was named for a place in the Hebrides islands, near where Gavin and Geddes saw it—became (as Sherlock Holmes's Dr. Watson used to say) "the talk of all England."

But no scientist, fisherman, or zoologist stepped forward to identify it.

No one knows what the Soay beast is. Today people still speculate upon it.

The Soay beast has shown one thing: that an entirely unknown monster, unsuspected to exist, can appear for the first time, or almost the first time, in these modern times. There were no rumors over fourteen hundred years about the Soay beast, as there have been about that other mystery in Scotland, the Loch Ness monster. In Loch Ness, Scotland, a large, unknown water beast has shown itself, every once in a while, over almost one and one-half thousand years.

When Geddes and Gavin saw the Soay beast, they became either the first men who ever did, or, at the very least, the first two who ever got a good look at it.

Dr. (of Science) Maurice Burton, who conducts "The World of Science" page in *The Illustrated London News,* brought the story to the attention of Britain and the world by reporting it at length in the issue of June 4, 1960.

Dr. Burton had asked Mr. Geddes for his account of the day the men saw the Soay beast.

Geddes told how he had started out in his boat to fish for mackerel. He'd seen Gavin perched on the rocks. He'd moved in to ask if Gavin would like to join him. Gavin did.

The men pulled away from the beach. The first monster they saw, as events unfolded, was a basking shark.

Galapagos Island tortoises, to 500 pounds, are world's biggest land tortoises, and one of most incredible creatures. One lived over 100 years in London Zoo. From St. Augustine, Florida, Alligator Farm.

The basking shark is the second-largest shark, 35 to 40 feet long, up to 8,600 pounds in weight. (The whale shark, known to reach 45 feet and reported up to 60 feet, is larger. A 38-foot whale shark caught at Knight's Key, Florida, weighed 26,594 pounds.) The basking shark is not particularly dangerous to man, for it feeds on plankton, tiny fish, and shrimplike crustaceans. But it could easily upset a boat. Even if it is not an imminent danger, it was, on that sunshiny day, an impressive sight —especially to Gavin, for whom any large sea creature was a completely new spectacle.

The next monster the men encountered was in the form of a group of five killer whales. From his experience at sea, Tex Geddes kept well away from them. Not quite as long as the basking shark gets, the killer reaches 20 to 35 feet in length. It has been described by Douglas Burden as "the most formidable predator on this planet."

"Certainly," Burden goes on, "no creature that swims begins to equal the killer whale in ferocity and strength. He can be . . . rightfully compared with the king of the tyrant dinosaurs, *Tyrannosaurus rex,* that dominated his age on land 80 million years ago.

"*Tyrannosaurus* was probably the most terrible engine of destruction the world has ever seen, but while *Tyrannosaurus* had a minute brain, the killer whale is a remarkably intelligent animal. They often hunt in packs with teamlike precision. As soon as a killer is sighted Eskimos head for shore, for they know that he is to be feared above all animals. . . . His entire form, compact like a lethal torpedo, breathes speed and power. He is vicious and sinister and smart. His great dorsal fin cuts

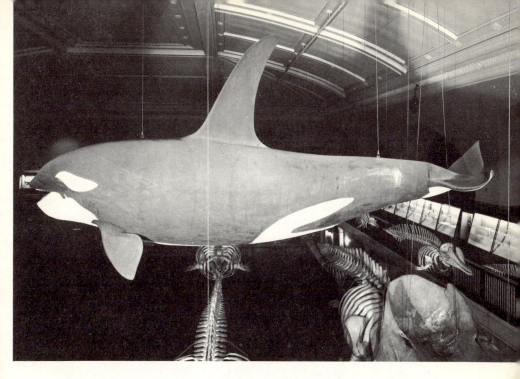

Killer whale, up to 30 feet long, is the largest of the so-called dolphins. Female, only 15 feet long, produces 7-foot offspring. Killer is one of most destructive killing machines of animal kingdom.

the water six feet above his back, flaunting his banner like the telltale periscope of a prowling submarine.

"In the Arctic and Antarctic, killer whales skirt the ice and sometimes rise vertically with heads six to eight feet above the surface, looking for prey. And when they find it they strike the floes with their great backs and smash them to pieces in order to dump seal or penguin or any living creature into the water. Killers have been seen throwing enormous bull sea lions fifteen feet into the air—playing with them like a cat with a mouse. Like the wolf and the tiger, the killer lives by attack and his capacity is almost incredible." In the stomach of one 21-foot killer, thirteen porpoises and fourteen seals were reported. A fifteenth seal was in the killer's throat.

During one of Robert Falcon Scott's Antarctic expeditions, killer whales demonstrated their terrifying strength. Some of Scott's sled dogs were standing on an ice floe. Two killer whales attacked. They dived beneath the ice, and swam swiftly upwards. They struck the ice floe —two and a half feet thick—with such force that the ice shattered. The dogs barely scampered away. An Antarctic photographer, H. G. Ponting, once was nearly killed when killers smashed into the ice he was standing on.

So it was for good and sufficient reasons that Tex Geddes kept his small boat far apart from the killers. Besides, the mackerel were playing on the surface all around the dinghy. Geddes was concentrating on fishing.

Then, he said, he noticed "a large black shape on the surface of the water away over towards the Skye shore, probably two miles from where we were fishing."

That was the first appearance of that day's Monster No. 3, the entirely unknown one, the Soay beast.

"Although," Geddes continued, "the object seemed to be in the general direction of where we had last seen the killers I did not think it was one of them, for neither its shape nor its behavior seemed right. It was too high out of the water in the first place and it remained on the surface for several minutes at a time."

The monster headed towards the two men in the boat.

"When the object appeared to be steaming towards us, we both stood up for a better view.

Close-up of a tag that solved a mystery: Fastened to a female green turtle at Tortuguero, Costa Rica, August 15, 1959, it was recovered by a fisherman 800 miles away off Cuba. It proved turtles cross oceans.

"I can't remember exactly how close it was when I heard the breathing, but I certainly could hear it before I could definitely have said that the object was alive. . . . It was not making much speed, maybe 3 or 4 knots. . . .

"I am afraid we both stared in amazement as the object came towards us, for this beast steaming slowly in our direction was like some hellish monster of prehistoric times.

"The head was definitely reptilian, about 2 feet 6 inches high, with large protruding eyes."

An artist, drawing a picture afterwards, based on Mr. Geddes' description, came up with a beast with a large, somewhat turtlelike head, a long neck, and a single big hump of a body with a ridge of saw-teeth-like bumps along the backbone.

Mr. Geddes continued: "There was at least two feet of clear water behind the neck, less than a foot of which we could see, and the creature's back, which rose sharply to its highest point some three to four feet out of the water and fell away gradually toward the after end.

"I would say we saw 8 to 10 feet of back on the water line . . . it was soon parallel with the dinghy, at a distance of twenty yards . . . it was constantly turning its head from side to side, as if surveying all around it . . . in profile the head appeared rather blunt and much darker than the rest of the body [which] seemed to be scaly and the top of its back was surmounted by an immense saw-toothed ridge. . . . It seemed to breathe through its mouth, which opened and shut with great regularity, and once when it turned towards us, I could see into its cavernous red maw. . . . I saw no teeth. . . .

"There was surprisingly little disturbance in the water as it passed, even when it submerged, as it did from time to time. Submerging was quite a graceful movement; it arched its neck and leisurely put its head under the surface, the head completely disappearing before there was any appreciable movement from the body, which slid below the surface like a seal. . . . Within seconds the head would break surface again and come clean out of the water before the body reappeared.

"During one of its dives we clearly saw a large darker piece sticking up well aft, whether this was some sort of fin, whether a flipper or a foot, your guess is as good as mine.

"It was only when it was swimming away from us

Ocean sunfish might have been Soay beast off Scotland. Up to 8 feet long and 1,200 pounds in weight, it gives birth to young 1/10th of an inch long. The young, growing up, increase in weight 60 million times.

that we were able to see that the creature's body, although 4 to 5 feet broad at the waterline, rose sharply to almost a knife-edge at the top of the back. . . .

"We watched it," Geddes estimated, "for well over an hour."

James Gavin, the London engineer who had hitchhiked with Geddes and was experiencing the most gripping hour of the most remarkable day of his lifetime, also gave Dr. Burton his eyewitness story.

"At the waterline," Gavin said, "the body was 6 to 8 feet long." (Geddes had said 8 to 10.) "It was hump-shaped, rising to a centrally placed apex about 2 feet high," Gavin continued.

"The line of the back was formed by a series of triangular-shaped spines, the largest at the apex and reducing in size to the waterline. The spines appeared to be solid and immobile—they did not resemble fins. . . .

"The neck appeared to be cylindrical and, at a guess, about 8 inches in diameter. It arose from the water about 12 inches forward of the body. I could not see where they joined; about 15 to 18 inches of neck was visible. . . . Head and neck arose to a height of about 2 feet. At intervals the head and neck went forward and submerged. They would then re-emerge, the large gaping mouth would open (giving the impression of a large melon with a quarter removed) and there would be a series of very loud, roaring whistling noises as it breathed.

"After about five minutes the beast submerged with a forward diving motion—I thought I saw something follow the body down.

"It later resurfaced about a quarter of a mile further out to sea and I then watched it until it disappeared in the distance."

Several things, Dr. Burton thought, stood out about the eyewitness descriptions given by Geddes and Gavin.

First, they were remarkably detailed, much more detailed than most descriptions of monsters spotted at sea. There was nothing vague about them. (I would say that Gavin and Geddes, after their solid hour of watching the

Green turtle, here being tagged by Dr. Archie Carr of University of Florida, has been shown by Carr to cross South Atlantic from Ascension to Brazil. How? Trips probably involve celestial navigation.

monster, have come up with the most complete description we have of any of the world's unknown animals. They have provided more eyewitness details than we have, for instance, on the Loch Ness monster.) Second, the two men, who were contacted separately, agreed remarkably well on the details they saw. Third, the two descriptions, though useful, were not conclusive evidence. Skulls, skins, and skeletons, or a captured live specimen, are needed to prove what the Soay beast is.

What might it be? An immediate possibility that comes to mind is a giant tortoise. There were huge (20-foot-long) turtles in prehistoric times, as we know from bones that have been dug up. Today, the leathery turtle (or leatherback or trunkback), which lives in the sea, has been confirmed at 8 feet long, and a weight of nearly a ton, and there have been reports of its reaching 10 feet. It is the biggest known turtle. A leatherback caught off Canada weighed 1,450 pounds and had a front-flipper spread of 8 feet. But the neck of the leathery turtle, short and thick, is not like the long neck that Gavin and Geddes saw.

Other great marine turtles—the hawksbill (which furnishes tortoise shell), the green turtle (which furnishes soup), the ridley, or the loggerhead—also seem to have the wrong kind of neck.

Turtles live in tropical seas, but the leathery turtle sometimes visits British waters, and in 1938 a ridley turtle, previously known only on the American side of the Atlantic, and recorded from the Gulf of Mexico to Massachusetts, was cast ashore on the coast of Ireland. Only recently, Dr. Archie Carr of the University of Florida proved that the green turtle makes long sea

THE SOAY BEAST

voyages. A student of his tagged green turtles on Ascension Island. Four of those bearing the tags were later picked up fourteen hundred miles down the Atlantic from Ascension, in Brazil.

The unknown monster Gavin and Geddes saw may, of course, be that other unknown monster (or group of monsters), the sea serpent. It may be the same as the unknown submarine-sized sea monster with a long neck and protruding eyes that Sam Randazzo, of the seiner *Endeavor,* in 1953 said he saw from only fifteen feet away off San Pedro, California. But any identification that says that one unknown animal is another unknown animal only compounds the mystery.

Another possibility is that the Soay beast was a *Varanus* lizard. That's what the Komodo dragon is. The Komodo dragon is a 10-foot-long Asiatic mystery monster. It lives only in the four small East Indies islands. It may have reached them by swimming across small stretches of ocean to get there. How it could have managed to get from Asia to Scotland poses a problem. It might have been helped along by the Gulf Stream. It it was, then it probably came not from Asia but from South America, where it isn't supposed to be.

If the Soay beast came from South America, it could be something like the marine iguanas, 5-foot-long lizards with rows of spines on their backs, of the Galápagos islands off Ecuador. These islands are in the Pacific, and how a beast could get from *there* to the British Isles is another stumper.

The common 6-foot-long iguana of South America could reach the Atlantic and perhaps ride the Gulf stream and so might just possibly emulate the ridley and the green turtle and cross the ocean. But both Gavin and Geddes thought the Soay beast was much larger than the iguana. Geddes estimated that the Soay beast weighed 5 tons. There is, of course, the likely possibility that the animal looked larger in the water than it was.

There is the outside chance that the Soay beast was a South American iguana, but one much larger than any iguana known to exist. If so, there is an unknown iguana for scientists to chase down. At least one huge iguana, never identified, has been rumored to exist.

James Gavin, after his vacation had unexpectedly turned into the adventure of his lifetime and into a major scientific mystery, heard that the crews of two lobster boats, fishing near Scotland, had seen something like the Soay beast, "much to their consternation," he was told.

Searching the records, Dr. Burton found a few skimpy records of turtlelike unknown creatures at sea.

Three of these actually were seen in waters near Scotland.

Something that looked like an unknown turtlelike beast recently was found, dead, on the shore in Australia. Occasionally, other great hulks of flesh—up to many tons—have been washed ashore and not identified. Frequently, they have decomposed too far to tell what they were. Not all the animals living in the sea, though, are washed ashore. One that was was the giant squid. This is a ten-armed octopuslike creature that may reach over 50 feet long and that man never has caught alive and knows only because several times it has been washed onto the beach, sometimes during great storms—and because it is eaten by sperm whales.

Back in 1895, near the Azores islands, Prince Albert of Monaco was collecting oceanographic data. A whaling crew chased a sperm whale under his yacht. The whale surfaced, and vomited up its last meal: undigested parts of a giant squid.

Whaling ships have found parts of many other giant squids inside sperm whales that have been caught.

So far it has not been possible to identify the Soay beast. But from the detailed descriptions given by Geddes and Gavin, and from their striking agreement with each other, the best bet seems to be that the Soay beast is another one of the world's unknown monsters, another large animal so far uncaptured, unkilled (by men), and unknown to science. Diver-photographer Hans Hass explains:

"The sea does not willingly reveal its secrets. We are often asked how it is that when diving we are able to avoid the great creatures that inhabit the waters. However, to tell the truth, it has always been much easier to avoid them than to find them."

THE GREAT GROANING WORMS

What looks like a length of garden hose on the ground in Gippsland, in the state of Victoria, southern Australia, instead may be the giant earthworm. The worm, lying on the earth, may even appear as motionless as the garden hose. It is notoriously slow-moving above ground—but not beneath the surface.

Mildred Bellomy and a friend went hunting the giant worms—which are 4 or 6 feet long, reportedly even up to 10 or 11 feet long, and ¾ of an inch thick. The object was to collect the worms as food for the friend's pet: a platypus named Gluttonous Teddy.

The ground beneath her feet told Mildred Bellomy the worms were in it. "I soon learned," she said, "that 'listening to the earthworms play' is no meaningless phrase. During wet spells, or very early in the morning on a

Snake or worm? Pioneers in Australia asked this question about Australia's giant earthworm. One worm taken not long ago measured 42 inches alive, after death reached 5 feet. Others are said to grow longer.

normal day, the worms are quite near the surface. They are quite sensitive to footstep vibrations, and wherever we walked, we heard weird groaning gurgles as the giants retreated into their water-logged burrows."

The ground, when filled with the giant worms, others have reported, sounds like bathtubs emptying.

Mysteries still surround the worm. Does he serve any ascertainable purpose as does the ordinary earthworm? It's possible that his huge tunnels help drain the damp and heavy soils he inhabits. Does he smell? He has been reported as having an odor something like creosote. Some persons believe this applies only to those worms that were contaminated with creosote when sleepers for a railway were laid, and is not a natural smell for the worm at all. Is the worm dying out? Possibly so. But the worm may not be encountered so frequently by men simply because men in the part of Australia where the worm lives are building fewer roads, bridges, or fences than they used to, and these activities were the sort that turned up the most worms in former days. Another question is what, besides the kookaburra and the platypus, eats the great worm. There is one old illustration of a duck consuming one, and one farmer reported an eel eating a giant earthworm about as large as the eel itself.

The worms managed to avoid men entirely—they stayed hidden and were unknown and undreamed of—till just around one hundred years ago. How they managed to do so is perfectly clear from the ways they avoid capture today.

As you dig for him, the giant worm often flees away from you through his network of burrows. He is helped along by a milky fluid he exudes from pores on his back.

He slips through the earth rapidly, and often escapes you, because he is a self-lubricated animal. The same liquid defends the worm, science has recently learned, from small parasites and soil bacteria.

Mildred Bellomy and her friend wielded their spades.

They dug into dozens of burrows. The worms always got away.

Finally they caught a worm with part of his body exposed. They grabbed him.

The worm squirted out his fluid. The worm actually can shoot it out, about a foot, in all directions. He did. The fluid made him hard to hold.

But he was held—and tied into a knot. The knot was big enough so that the worm couldn't draw it back into the ground.

The two hunters knew enough not to start pulling out the worm.

This does not work, as even the kookaburra, or laughing jackass, an Australian bird, knows just as well as do men. The laughing jackass has its own method of unearthing the giant worms.

The kookaburra, which is a large kingfisher, is 17½ inches long, or about twice as big as a starling or slightly shorter than the 19-inch-long American crow. Besides the giant worms, the kookaburra eats snakes. It is said to be a very husky bird. It must be, because it puts a lot of work into capturing the giant worm.

In his tunnel in the ground the worm can swell up at either end of his body, fill the tunnel, and thus make it all but impossible to haul him out.

In addition, the worm's resistance is increased by tiny spinules, or setae, about one thirty-sixth of an inch in length, that project from his skin and dig into the tunnel walls. These setae also are used by the worm to move backward or forward—he can travel in either direction—through his tunnels.

In short, when he clings inside his burrow, the giant earthworm is one of the world's most immovable objects.

This the kookaburra has discovered. The bird spies a part of a worm above ground and pounces down upon it. The bird grabs the part, braces itself, and waits. The worm, of course, has puffed up inside his tunnel, and his setae are helping hold him in.

The kookaburra simply hangs on until the worm slackens a bit. Then the bird gives a quick tug. More of the worm slips from the burrow.

This goes on quite a while. Finally, the whole worm is outside. He now is sluggish. And the kookaburra can dine.

Because the worm is too big for the kookaburra to fly away with, the bird makes his meal right where it is.

Mildred Bellomy and her companion, having tied the worm into a knot, could not do just exactly as the kookaburra does. Besides, the worm has still another defense: The worm has 350 to 500 rings, or segments, and the worm is brittle. Some of the segments can break off in your hand and then the great worm can scoot away through his tunnel.

So the rest of the worm had to be dug out with spades. It was a job, what with the twists of the burrow. These wind so much that men digging up the worm unearth a few separate pieces of worm more often than the entire beast.

The entire worm at length was excavated.

How to catch a giant earthworm: You tie part of it into knots so worm can't crawl into ground, get away. Incredible as it seems, it is reported that if giant worm's head is cut off, a new one will grow.

Gluttonous Teddy, the platypus, was at last assured of a meal. The platypus could consume all of the worm except that the head, which has a transverse slit of a mouth, a quarter of an inch wide, and is extremely tough, had to be sliced up before Gluttonous Teddy could manage it.

The first human beings to come across the Gippsland worm seem to have been surveyors for a railroad, in the Brandy Creek district, back in 1868.

These pioneers argued around many campfires before they got around to sending specimens to Professor

Frederick McCoy, director of the National Museum of Australia, with their question:

"Is it a snake or a worm?"

McCoy said it was a worm. In the first number of the *Natural History of Australia,* he gave the animal a Latin name: *Megascolides australis.*

Since that time, scientists have discovered more facts about *Megascolides australis.* The eggs are known. They are 2 to 3 inches long, or about the length of a hen's egg. They are up to three quarters of an inch in diameter. At one end there is a bunch of filaments. At the other end there is a short and pointed extension. The eggs are greenish and translucent when fresh. Then they become dark brown.

The egg is shaped something like a cocktail sausage. The worm inside it—there is just one—will be from 6 to 10 or 12 inches long when he comes out.

When *Megascolides australis* is exhibited, some men and women turn away. The animal looks repulsive. A huge edition of the earthworm in your yard, *Megascolides* has dirty pinkish flesh and a firm and darker front (or mouth); it gradually enlarges for the first dozen segments or so and then the worm becomes for 2 or 3 inches still more swollen and purplish brown.

Complete mystery is whether or not *Megascolides australis* is—as he often has been assumed to be—the largest worm in the world. He may be the heaviest. He is certainly not the longest. Actually, men are only now becoming familiar with the worms that inhabit the earth, and new monstrous ones are frequently identified. An ocean animal, a proboscis worm, has great powers to contract or expand its body, and one of the longest measured 80 to 90 feet when fully extended. A tapeworm that

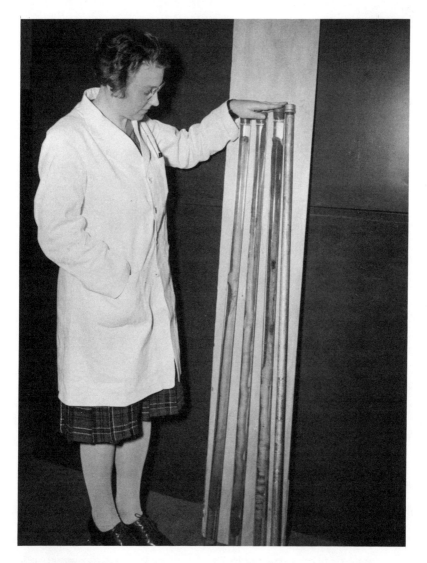

Giant earthworms are shipped in glass tubes to laboratories for study. It is not known what purpose in nature the great, groaning worms serve. They may help drain the damp heavy soils they live in.

lives in fish gets to be 60 feet long; one in cattle grows to as long as 100 feet. These, of course, are not earthworms. *Megascolides australis,* when all the facts are in, may not even be the biggest earthworm. Other monster earthworms have been reported in the alpine region of the Indian Ocean island of Ceylon, in southern India, in Africa, and recently in the South American Andes by Marté Latham.

Mrs. Latham, an American, brought back alive from Colombia a worm she called "a real monster, 5½ feet long." Newspaper reporters called the worm Gertrude. Mrs. Latham sent Gertrude on to the London Zoological Society. Gertrude arrived in London, June 11, 1961. Zoologists, who believed Gertrude was a prehistoric type, hoped she would give them a chance at serious research. Gertrude didn't; she died July 21, 1961.

As if all these worms to compete with *Megascolides australis* were not enough, Australia itself has unearthed another giant mystery worm. In 1939, forestry workers making new roadways in northern New South Wales first reported these creatures. In the late 1940's, fragments of the new breed of worms reached the Australian museum. Not till May 1957 did the first scientific expedition go out after the new worms, now called Kyogle worms after a place near where they were found.

It took bulldozers, which can turn over tons of dirt and knock down many trees in a few hours, to expose forty-four Kyogle worms. The Kyogle worm proved somewhat shorter (about 4 feet in length) than *Megascolides australis,* but the Kyogle monster was somewhat thicker in spots.

For good measure, the very same scientific expedition

came back with still other different kinds of worms to study: (1) one that resembled the common garden earthworm; (2) a salmon-pink creature called the spaghetti worm on account of its long body, no thicker than that of an ordinary earthworm but over one foot long; (3) another worm striped in cream and black crossbands, like a football jersey. This last worm appeared rare. Only one specimen was seen.

As for *Megascolides* itself, there are still arguments about how big it really is: 2 feet long, when contracted, and about 6 feet, when extended, said Professor McCoy, the man who named it in 1868; on the average, 44 to 48 inches alive, said Sir Baldwin Spencer—his largest measured 56 inches alive. One recently caught measured 42 inches alive, but after death, held up by one end, was pulled by gravity to a length of nearly 5 feet. "I have seen," writes Charles Barrett in the *Bulletin of the New York Zoological Society,* March-April 1938, "many specimens extending 7 feet when extended, and a number about 2 feet longer. My record *Megascolides* was over 10 feet." L. C. Cook, whose farm is home to many of the worms, says he has seen specimens 11 feet long, and thinks 13 feet is the probable limit.

Recently, the University of California and the Rothamstead Agricultural Station in England received giant earthworms from Australia so that scientific study might resolve questions about their size and other mysteries surrounding them. But even after the last word is in on *Megascolides,* it will be a long time before the rest of the big mystery worms of the world are collected and scientifically researched. It will be a long time before men are sure they know the worms beneath their feet.

THE YOUNG SEA SERPENT

One Morning in 1930, Anton Bruun, a youthful Danish sea scientist, discovered what has become the world's most mysterious eel.

The experience dominated the rest of Bruun's days.

Bruun was aboard the *Dana,* a research ship, off South Africa, when he made the acquaintance of the eel. It was the immature, or young form—the larva—of an entirely unknown eel that Bruun encountered. It was hauled aboard in a fishing net. The size of the larva was startling: It was 6 feet long. It appeared capable of growing into a real monster of the seas, an eel 50 or 100 or even 150 or 180 feet long, a monster fully the equal of any sea beast ever dreamed up by the most imaginative science fiction writer.

Bruun spent the rest of his life trying to answer one

question about the eel larva: Was the larva the young sea serpent?

He always thought the answer was *yes*.

To bring up the giant eel larva, the *Dana* had dropped her trawl about a mile down into the sea. She was not far from the Cape of Good Hope, and only a few miles from the position in the South Atlantic where, in 1848, Captain Peter M'Quhae and crew members of the British frigate *Daedalus* had sighted an enormous eel-like monster on the ocean's surface.

Anton Bruun, who never could wait for a new haul of specimens to be brought aboard, came out on deck when the net was about to be brought up. It was swung, wet and dripping, to the deck.

It held some strange samples of sea life: luminescent fish; fish with protruding eyes; fish with long antennae or feelers. Most were small.

But these were just ordinary weirdies from mile-deep water. The *Dana* had brought up a lot of queer fish before this. Bruun was unruffled. Then he saw something else. He began to gawk.

What he saw was a whopper. It was fully 6 feet long. Its coils were tangled in the net.

Neither Bruun nor anyone else recognized it. It was a large, unknown sea creature.

Bruun examined it.

He lifted it into his arms.

Then and later he studied its features and the structure of its bones. He began to have an idea what it was. After he had dissected it, he knew—and what he had learned surprised him:

It was the larva (the young) of an eel.

Among known eels, the conger and moray grow larger than others. A monster conger can grow, and in exceptional cases does grow, up to 8 or 10 feet long. Dr. Maurice Burton, in *Animal Legends,* says the record conger was about 11 feet long. The record moray, he says, was 16 feet long.

The larvae of these eels are 3 or 4 inches long—or about one thirtieth (or so) of their length as adults.

If the 6-foot larva grew proportionately as long as the conger grows, the result would be an eel 180 feet long.

But most animals never reach maximum size for their species. Ordinarily, the giant eel might be, say, something around 80 or 100 feet long.

That Bruun's larva could grow into that often reported

Sea serpents have been described by sailors since Erik Pontoppidan, Bishop of Bergen, Norway, in 1746 wrote the book from which this picture was taken. Anton Bruun thought they might be gigantic eels.

THE YOUNG SEA SERPENT

but never identified creature, the sea serpent, seems clear.

Such a giant eel might, like some known eels, live close to the bottom in moderately deep water (a mile deep, more or less). The eel might not rise to the surface at all except to mate or die. Its death struggle might be the writhing sometimes attributed to the sea serpent.

If the giant eel comes to the surface this rarely, this may explain why it never has been washed ashore. Many sea creatures have become known to man only when, at some time or another, they were tossed up onto the beach. There are, in fact, around eleven known whales that have been identified this way—whales that never or almost never are seen by whaling ships.

No sea serpent ever has been washed up.

Anton Bruun watched the rest of his life for another 6-foot eel larva and for the giant eel itself.

In 1950, Bruun, by then Denmark's leading sea scientist and internationally famous, was back in the Atlantic off the Cape of Good Hope aboard the Danish Navy's *Galathea,* another oceanographic research ship. Like Captain Ahab pursuing Moby Dick, the white sperm whale in Herman Melville's novel of the same name, Anton Bruun had been obsessed with his quarry for years.

Again and again he lowered his net.

When he failed to draw up another giant larva, he was of course disappointed. He thought maybe the *Galathea* had not searched in the right places. He thought maybe the eel would be more likely to be found in shallower water over the continental shelf. His reason: food supplies would be more plentiful in the shallower, offshore areas than in deeper water.

Dr. Bruun's 6-foot-long *Leptocephalus* (that's the

name of all larval forms of eel) had, its dissection showed, 450 rudimentary vertebral (or spinal) plates. The ordinary eel has 104. The larger conger eel has 150.

This great number of vertebral plates is another reason the larva could grow into a sea serpent.

The *Galathea* brought back sea creatures fully as surprising as a sea serpent would be. They included a monstrous angler fish (*Galathea thauma*), named for the ship, with what looks like neon tubes inside its mouth to lure smaller fish down its gullet. They included the *Trachyrincus,* shaped like a sweet potato, one of the deepest-living fishes. They included a previously unknown, fire-engine red shrimp from three miles down. They included a velvet-black, small fish shaped like a submarine. They included an unknown sea anemone (from six miles down), a white sea spider (from three miles down), a sea snake related to the deadly cobra, and a lobster without eyes (it couldn't use them in the blackness two miles down, where it lives). They included mussels, worms, and bacteria from the greatest depths.

But Dr. Bruun failed to get either another *Leptocephalus* or its giant parent.

Almost coincidentally with Dr. Bruun's 1930 discovery of the 6-footer, William Beebe, the American who made deep dives in the bathysphere, saw a much smaller specimen of an unknown larva of a salt-water eel. Beebe made a descent into the sea on June 11, 1930. He had reached 550 feet down, when, he said:

"A big *Leptocephalus* undulated past, a pale ribbon of transparent gelatin with only the two iridescent eyes to indicate its arrival. As it moved, I could see the outline faintly—10 inches long at least—and as it passed close, even the parted jaws were visible. This was the larva of some great sea eel."

Back in Copenhagen, after the 1930 voyage of the *Dana,* the 6-foot larva had been turned over to a scientist for further careful study. The researcher never finished his task. The larva was returned to Bruun. He took up the research. "But," Mr. R. Sparck of the University Zoological Museum in Copenhagen told me in July 1963, "he didn't manage to publish a paper on this interesting animal. So we are still lacking a scientific treatment and description, unfortunately."

That was why, after the first discovery of the larva in 1930, the world never heard anything else about it.

"If the monstrous larva exists," Bruun said, "the monstrous adults must exist, too—as terrifying as any sea serpent ever painted. I shall search for them again, and some day they will be found." To the end of his life, on December 13, 1961, he frequently said: "I am a man who rather believes in sea serpents."

THE BEAR'S-PAW CLAM

"We found, after looking around," said Wilbert McLeod Chapman, a fish research biologist, "that we were near the middle of a group of eleven of the monsters, which were scattered around us at 10- to 20-foot intervals, and we had not noticed them at all."

Chapman and Harlan Cheyne, another biologist, were in the ocean off a South Pacific island. They were out with their water goggles scouting for fish.

The monsters surrounding Chapman and Cheyne were giant bear's-paw clams, or man-eating clams, the world's biggest dreaded shellfish. The great clam is a mystery monster that is only now becoming known. Soldiers, sailors, airmen, and marines in the Pacific during World War II began to learn a bit about it. Since the war skin divers like Chapman and Cheyne have added more information.

Tridacna gigas's shell often weighs up to as much as 400 to 500 pounds, maybe in places like Australia's Great Barrier Reef up to 1,000 pounds (half a ton), maybe even a ton. Exactly how huge it gets remains a mystery, but one thing is certain: it is the largest shell in the world.

The great shell is in two parts, hinged by a great adductor muscle. As the clam lies on the sea bottom, the hinge is downward. The clam is often partly hidden in coral, stone, or sand, and sometimes by murky water, which is why men like Chapman and Cheyne can come close upon the giant monster without realizing that it is there.

What sometimes happens next is what gives the bear's-paw that other name: man-eating.

A diver or swimmer can poke his arm or leg into the clam's mantle—the soft lining of the shell. It is the most natural thing in the world to do. A man underwater frequently reaches out for something to relieve the buoyancy of his body. Then the two sides of the great shell snap shut on the intruding arm or leg.

Then the clam hangs on.

It is not a man-eater. But it can kill you. A man in the grip of the clam can easily be held underwater till he drowns. The South Pacific is full of native tales about pearl divers or other men disappearing due to meeting up with *Tridacna gigas*.

Chapman measured one of the giant clams that surrounded Cheyne and himself. It was about 2½ feet high, 3 feet long, and 1½ feet thick. There was an 8-inch gap between the corrugated lips of the shell—wide enough to stick your hand in, or wide enough to step into. The corrugations on each side of the shell, Chapman noticed, fitted into each other when the shell shut. The drab shell was difficult to see against its sea-bottom background.

He had been swimming near the bottom, alongside an open reef, when he encountered the clam.

"I bumped against a coral head," he said. "It snapped shut with a thud that was clearly heard under the water and which startled me, for this was the first time that a coral head had ever attempted to bite back.

"It was not a coral head at all but one of the giant clams."

Bear's-paw clam, which has strength to hold a man under water and drown him, is shown here almost blending into coral stocks off New Guinea. Photo by American Museum of Natural History.

He called Cheyne. The two men, after discovering the eleven clams in the vicinity, decided to experiment with one of them.

Nearby was a stick of coral about the thickness of a large broom handle. They stuck it into the clam's mantle.

"The animal would snap shut," Chapman wrote in *Fishing in Troubled Waters* (J. B. Lippincott, Company, Philadelphia and New York, 1949), "at the lightest touch on the mantle and break the heavy coral stick like a straw. Rapping on the shell would make it close, or a shadow passing over the top of the shell would have the same effect."

Chapman, who is a 230-pounder and is 6 feet 3 inches tall, got a healthy respect for the bear's-paw clam the day he met it.

"Of the group of clams that we found," he wrote, "none was in water more than five feet deep, and some were in sufficiently shallow [water] so that they were just under the surface at low tide. If a person did get caught by a clam and had a long knife with him, it would probably be possible to reach down into the clam and cut the great adductor muscle and free himself, if he were in such a position that he could get his head above water and catch a breath.

"It would probably take a couple of minutes of hacking because the muscle is thicker than your wrist and if one were caught so that his head could not reach the surface, then it would most likely be the end.

"It was not possible for the two of us pushing against the side of the clam to roll it over or even to budge it. After playing around with them for a time we decided that it would be best to keep our eyes open for them while working around the reef. We never saw one again."

The clam may not be as dangerous as the natives' tales from the South Pacific say it is. Says *Sea Secrets* of the International Oceanographic Foundation (University of Miami), "It has been reported to trap divers or waders by their feet by clamping its heavy shells shut, but there is no factual account of such an incident."

If a man were caught by the clam, he might be badly hurt. "One of the big *Tridacnas* closing up on a man's leg," wrote A. Hyatt Verrill, "will cut deeply into the flesh and snap and crush the bones."

Tridacna shells have been used as baptismal fonts in missionary stations, and some serve similar purposes in churches in Europe. These are the littlest *Tridacna* shells. The big ones are usually left on the reef or sea floor. They are too heavy to move.

The mantle, or shell lining, was reported by Wilbert Chapman to be variously colored. "The one which we first discovered was a delicate light-olive color with the texture and look of velvet, and dusted over its surface were light blue specks. Another was predominantly light blue with darker blue spots upon it. No two clams had the same color on their mantles." "Large, fleshy, brightly colored," was another description of the mantle. "Spots suggesting eyes."

The specks, or little bright spots, on the mantle are one of the most amazing things about the bear's-paw clam—and about any animal on earth.

"These are actually 'skylights,'" wrote Ralph Buchsbaum and Lorus J. Milne in *The Lower Animals, Living Invertebrates of the World* (Doubleday & Company, Inc.,

Shell of bear's-paw clam is demonstrated by W. D. Cobb in American Museum of Natural History photo. Clam is found on Great Barrier Reef, off Australia. It actually raises a crop of tiny plants for its meals.

Garden City, New York), "admitting energy from the sun into 'greenhouses' within the mantle.

"In these spaces, microscopic green algae [plants] grow. . . . *Tridacna* uses its white blood cells to harvest the algae and, as an adult animal, seems not to use its digestive tract. It depends instead upon the plant food raised in the exposed parts of its body."

In other words, the clam, instead of eating you, grows its own food crop—single-celled plants—on its own flesh. The clam thus is a sort of farmer. It gets other food by filtering microscopic animals and other microscopic plants from the surrounding sea.

Animals obtain their food in many ways, but for one to grow its own crops in the folds of its own body is one of the most astonishing.

There are large clams off both East and West coasts of the U.S.—but nothing like as big as *Tridacna gigas*.

In Puget Sound and off northern California, you can find clams up to 16 or 18 inches long and weighing 15 pounds. Some, the Washington clams of Puget Sound, are edible.

Off the country's eastern shore, you can find surf clams 7 or 8 inches long and up to 2 or 3 pounds. They look clumsy. But they leap out of a boat with no difficulty. All of these clams, like *Tridacna,* are bivalves (the shell is in two parts).

There could be univalve—one-part—shells as big as *Tridacna,* but, if so, no one has located them. The biggest single shells known, nearly 2 feet long, come out of very deep water.

Roy Chapman Andrews, of the American Museum of

Natural History, met the giant clam as he paddled over a coral reef off of the Celebes, East Indies.

"I jabbed my paddle deep into the innocent-looking mass," he said. "The jaws snapped shut and held the paddle in a viselike grip. It was impossible to get it out; I had to break it off. As near as I could estimate this clam was about 3 feet across."

The American Museum has a *Tridacna* on exhibit that is 3 feet in diameter and weighs 597½ pounds. The Raffles Museum, Singapore, has one 3 feet across. "Off the coast of Australia," Mr. Andrews said, "it is reported that they reach a length of 6 feet and a weight of nearly a ton."

Leonard Wibberley told of his adventures with the giant clam: "I dove down to inspect it. The mantle, as I recall it, was a lovely green with here and there spots of white or gold upon it. This mantle . . . had three holes in it through which the clam sucked in sea water from which to strain its food, the water being exhausted through a valve near the hinge of the shell. I took a little piece of coral and dropped it into one of the holes. Immediately the hole puckered up, like the lips of someone who has taken something disagreeable into his mouth, and a second later the coral was spat out with surprising force."

When Mr. Wibberley tapped the clam's shell, the two halves came immediately and firmly together.

Hans Hass, a Viennese, met the great clam not long ago off the Great Barrier Reef of Australia. Constructed by coral animals, the Great Barrier Reef is by far the largest structure built by any living creatures (including men) upon this earth: It is 1,200 miles long, gets 100 miles wide and, "has a volume 8 million times greater than that of the Pyramid of Cheops at Giza, a hundred thousand times greater than that of the Great Wall of China, and two thousand times greater than the whole mass of the City of New York."

Hass was surprised by the size of the animals he encountered on the Great Barrier Reef. Yellow sea cucumbers resembled pumpkins, deep blue starfish got up to 16 or 20 inches across. His giant clams were over 3 feet across. One reason the clams lie open in shallow water, he points out, is to obtain sunlight for the tiny plants it grows for food in the skin and tissues of its own body.

Hass and his wife, Lotte, wondered what, exactly, the bear's-paw clam would do to a leg, and decided to make an experiment to find out. They decided to bait the clam with a leg. The leg they used for the purpose was a lady's leg, but not Lotte's. It was an artificial department-store leg used to display nylons.

The leg was plastic. They filled it with plaster. "Maybe it was not quite fair to experiment with a peg leg," Hass wrote, in *We Come from the Sea* (Doubleday & Company, Inc., Garden City, New York, 1959), "for it had hardly any joint and besides that was much too hard. All the same it was a leg and we could not find a better one.

"I shoved the leg in between the open shells and then pulled it—as quickly as a man might do who inadvertently steps into a trap—out again," Hass said, "or, rather, I tried to pull it out, but the clam had snapped together and held on fast. The more I tugged, and wrenched, and hauled, the tighter the edges of the shell stuck together. . . . I noticed some signs of relaxation and then I gave a sudden jerk, but the clam was quicker than I was.

"After thirty-five minutes we decided to give up, so we attached the *Tridacna* to a rope and hauled it up into shallow water." He tried to lever the shell apart with a harpoon, but could not. "I fixed a knife to the end of a stick and (cut) through the powerful . . . muscles. Finally we got the leg free and could see what had happened to it.

"The edges of the shells had cut right into the plaster on both sides."

There were a lot of cracks all around the leg. They were enough to convince Hass. Ever since, he has been mighty careful not to step on a bear's-paw clam.

OUR FIRST ANIMALS FROM OUTER SPACE?

Does life exist on other worlds? Are there little green men on other planets? Are there the bug-eyed monsters of H. G. Wells? Are there three- or four-headed or other weird animals of species we cannot even imagine? Will our spacemen, when they step onto the moon or Mars, find living things—animals or plants?

For over 2,600 years, men have argued over the question, "Is there life on other worlds?"

Now, thanks to the work of a handful of scientists, we can say *yes*. We have the first positive indication. The evidence—more of it is coming in all the time—is beginning to mount.

When astronaut John Glenn, in his three-orbit flight, saw "fireflies" outside his Mercury capsule, people wondered if they were our first space animals. Colonel Glenn never said that they were, and, it turned out, they were not.

But, in some leading U.S. and foreign laboratories, scientists, sparked by Drs. Warren G. Meinschein of Esso Research and Engineering Company and Bartholomew Nagy and Douglas Hennessy of Fordham University, have been studying meteorites, which we are sure came from somewhere in space.

Inside the meteorites, the scientists, some of whom worked entirely separately from the others, have found two proofs of life on other celestial bodies:

1) Chemical substances were found that, on the earth, are produced only by living things—plants, animals, or human bodies. The obvious assumption is that a living body put them there.

2) Mircofossils were found that appear to be tiny animals or plants or fragments of them. The fossils look like some creatures that resemble the tiniest, one-celled animals or plants on this earth. But the little fossils are not just the same as any known on the globe. They appear to be from out of this world.

On this earth, simple life—primitive, one-celled animals and plants—exist along with more complicated and intelligent creatures, including animals and human beings.

The situation may be the same on other celestial bodies.

In a recent book, *Life in the Universe,* authors Patrick Moore and Francis Jackson explain: "The suggestion that somewhere in the universe there may be a race of intelligent beings with three heads each and a dozen legs is *not* necessarily absurd."

The evidence for extraterrestrial life, says Dr. Harold C. Urey, a Nobel prize-winning scientist, is "better now than it was before." Of the discovery of life outside the earth, a discovery that in a few years may be proved beyond all doubt, he says, "This would be the most interesting and astounding fact of all scientific study in recent years."

What has happened so far is exciting:

The first American to see what probably were the first animals or plants from space was a man named George Claus. No, he was not a spaceman, and he was not looking out of the window of a Mercury spacecraft 150 miles above the globe. Instead, he was peering through a modern, high-powered microscope at bits of meteorites.

We don't know where, in space, meteorites came from, or even exactly what they are. They may be fragments of collisions between large or small cosmic bodies. The ages of some meteorites have been determined to be about 5 billion years, the estimated age of the earth. Many of the objects from space attracted by the earth's gravity are vaporized or burned in the atmosphere. Unlike a space capsule, a meteorite does not have a heat shield. But some of these objects from space do survive the hot plunge and end up in museums.

Dr. Claus examined particles of four meteorites from France, from India, and from Tanganyika, Africa. One he looked at has come to be known as the Orgueil meteorite. On the night of May 14, 1864, almost exactly one hundred years ago, this particular messenger from space arrived over France, near the town of Orgueil, and exploded. With a great flash of light and a prolonged crack of thunder, it arrived on earth so spectacularly that

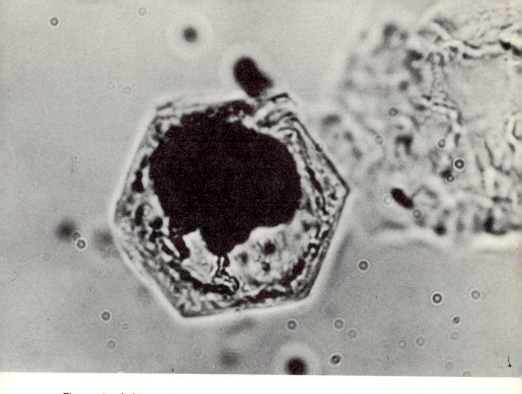

Tiny animal, big mystery: Are you gazing at the remains of one of the first animals man ever has seen from outer space? Tiny hexagonal fossil abounds in Orgueil, France, meteorite; is not found on earth.

thousands of people observed it. Pieces of it were picked up immediately.

A physicist and microbiologist at New York University, Dr. Claus first examined a piece of the Orgueil meteorite, and then the three others.

He found in all four what look like tiny fossils or fragments of fossils.

Some are single-celled structures that resemble algae (plants) found on earth.

One seems to have folded wings, like a bird's.

Another appears to be a jet-propelled creature—a pinpoint animal that may have moved by means of a jet as does the far larger octopus.

Some apparently have been caught by death in the act of cell division—dividing into two animals, the way one-celled creatures on earth reproduce themselves. You can actually see the partially split cell. It resembles two cells joined by a narrow bond.

Twenty chunks of the Orgueil meteorite were studied by laboratories and museums in the 1860's. Within these chunks scientists identified something very mysterious: organic carbon which some scientists felt had originated in living matter. But, the nineteenth-century scientists could not reach agreement on the origin of this carbon.

Then, in the 1870's, a German scientist, Otto Hahn, said he'd seen under a microscope what appeared to be fossils of organisms (living creatures) within fragments of meteorites. He got no one to listen to him. He wrote only one report. Today not much is known about his work. Otto Hahn was the only man in history who might have located space animals before George Claus did.

Altogether, Dr. Claus and his assistants found twenty-five different species—twenty-five kinds of tiny animals from space, if that is what they are. He found as many as seventeen hundred individual animals of a single species.

Fossils, before now, have given men their first clues to the existence of some animals.

Only a little over one hundred years ago, an English housewife found, by the side of the road, a fossil bone that her husband, a doctor, could not identify. That bone led on to the discovery of the first dinosaur we knew of,

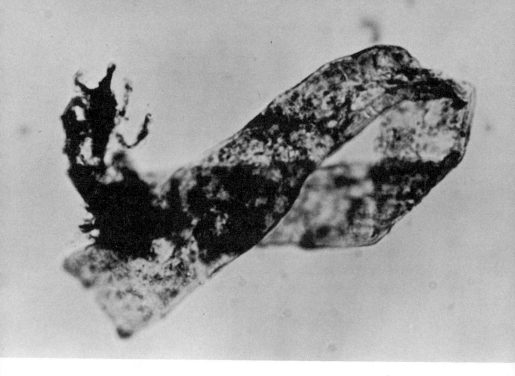

Ribbonlike tissue found in meteorites from outer space suggests forms found on earth. It may, therefore, have got into meteorite after meteorite reached earth. Other meteor fossils may be from space.

the iguanadont, and all the dinosaurs that were unearthed after. By today, we know of hundreds of species of dinosaurs.

Other fossil bones found during the excavation for the library at Princeton University, New Jersey, were the bones of a fish supposedly extinct for 75 million years. The fish, the coelacanth, has been caught since these bones were found, swimming off South Africa.

Other fossil bones obviously belonged to an unknown

whale. This whale remained unknown till one hundred of the species—the false killer—swam onto, and some grounded on, shallow sand near Kiel, Germany.

Though Dr. Claus may have been the first modern scientist to behold the fossils of space animals, he was not the first one to pick up the trail of life on other worlds.

Dr. Meinschein, a soft-spoken forty-two-year-old Kentuckian who learned organic chemistry at the Universities of Texas and Michigan, was not even thinking of space animals when he started out. He was thinking of petroleum. He, like many another researcher, was trying to find out where petroleum comes from. Is it the product of natural forces, like great heat and pressure far down in the earth? Or is petroleum all or partly from animal or vegetable remains? No one yet has fully explained.

In his experiments, Dr. Meinschein used a mass spectrometer. This instrument, linked with a computer, tells a scientist the number and arrangement of atoms within the molecules of a substance being examined.

Dr. Meinschein found hydrocarbon molecules that resembled each other in (1) soil waxes produced by animals and vegetables; (2) marine extracts, or sediments from the bottom of the sea; and (3) crude oil (petroleum).

In other words, some hydrocarbon molecules of crude oil were like hydrocarbon molecules found in living things, soils, and marine sediments.

Soils and marine sediments contain organic remnants of former life.

Petroleum, it follows, is likely to be proved in part a product of life. It contains hydrocarbon molecules that probably were made by ancient plants and animals because the same molecules are made by plants and animals today. Such molecules are, in essence, organic fossils.

At Fordham University, Dr. Bartholomew Nagy, who was also interested in the origins of petroleum, read one of Dr. Meinschein's papers. Nagy later met Meinschein. Nagy suggested that the Orgueil meteorite be subjected to a similar analysis. The idea was simply to find out what was inside the meteorite.

The men were not looking for signs of life.

A sample of the meteorite was obtained from Dr. Brian Mason, curator of the meteorite collection at the American Museum of Natural History. A piece of it was placed in a mass spectrometer at Esso Research and Engineering Company, where Dr. Meinschein is employed.

The first results were disappointing. There was too much water in the meteorite. Douglas Hennessy of Fordham found a way to distill off the extraterrestrial water. This water and the mineral content of the Orgueil meteorite were hints that there might be life-sustaining water, or seas, on the heavenly body the meteorite came from. This could be in itself significant: Evidence of a sea on another world means evidence of life, because the sea is a cradle and nursery of life as we know it.

With the water out of the meteorite, the experiment proceeded.

The mass spectrometer and a computer quickly told Drs. Meinschein, Nagy, and Hennessy that the hydrocarbon molecules in the Orgueil meteorite were similar to hydrocarbon molecules created on earth by living things.

The molecules usually had odd numbers of carbon atoms.

"The numbers 19, 21, and 23 occurred most fre-

Studying possibility of life in space, Elbert A. King, a moon surface technician of the National Aeronautics and Space Administration, works with Rosebud meteorite. Specimen belongs to University of Texas.

quently," the American Petroleum Institute reported. "This peaking is similar to the arrangements found . . . in such earth life as butter and the skin of apples. Here, then, were biotic [living] compounds, materials representing life which is already formed and functioning."

"We were astounded," Dr. Meinschein told me when I visited him at Esso Research's Linden, New Jersey, laboratories, "when we realized that these hydrocarbons showed signs of a biological origin."

He and his colleagues from Fordham had not set out to find life. They had simply taken a look inside a meteorite to see what they could see. And they got a trace of life: a chemical compound, like a wax, or paraffin, similar to substances produced in plants, animals, or human bodies.

They were at this point like a detective who has found the first bloodstain on the rug.

Two things, Dr. Meinschein told me, probably made the discovery of the first signs of life in meteorites possible. He thinks that the hydrocarbons that gave him and his associates, Drs. Nagy and Hennesy, their first clue are very long-lived—they can retain their structures in certain types of sediments for millions of years. And he thinks a few meteorites, the Orgueil and only several others, have not been subjected internally to high temperatures and have reached the earth with their contents less burned up than is the case with most meteorites.

At this point, Dr. Meinschein and the Fordham men reported their first result to the New York Academy of Science. After newspaper stories about the Academy of Science meeting, Dr. Meinschein heard from a man in California who asserted he knew all about life in outer space. On his trips to other worlds, the man wrote, he had become acquainted with the beings that inhabited them.

Dr. Meinschein intensified his efforts. He was often in his office on Saturdays, on hands and knees, comparing data on graphs fourteen feet long. He quickly found something else: evidence of another organic (living) substance in the Orgueil meteorite—a hydrocarbon that appears to be structurally related to cholesterol.

Cholesterol is found in the human body.

That was Bloodstain No. 2 on the rug.

A haunting question now troubled Meinschein, Nagy, and Hennessy: They had come upon evidence of animals —the chemicals produced by living things—but where were the animals?

It was the age-old, agonizing question of the hunter, zoologist, explorer, or scientist as he picks up the trail of an animal.

"The scientists," the Standard Oil Company (New Jersey) reported in the summer issue of its company magazine, *The Lamp,* in 1962, "realized that they were looking, not at life itself, but at virtual proof that somewhere life had existed outside the earth."

What would microscopic examination of the meteorite show?

That led to George Claus's microscopic examination of an Orgueil particle and of other meteorites—and to Dr. Claus's becoming the first American ever to see fossils from space.

After Claus found his twenty-five species of fossils, samples of the meteorites were sent to Calgary, Alberta, Canada, for examination by Dr. Frank Staplin, a specialist in fossil research in the laboratory of Imperial Oil Limited.

Dr. Staplin discovered half a dozen additional species of apparent animals or plants. The total reached thirty-one kinds.

Dr. Staplin, acquainted as he is with the assemblages of microfossils in sediments on earth, is sure that the assemblage from the meteorite did not come from earth. Although the meteorite fossils appear to him to be some-

OUR FIRST ANIMALS FROM OUTER SPACE? 159

thing like the forms of primitive terrestrial life, they are not the same as any known earthly species.

Not all scientists think that the little objects in the meteorites are fossils. Some assert they were made chemically, and were not once living animals or plants at all. Two scientists thought that some, at least, of the particles in the Orgueil meteorite were simply ragweed, juniper, or unidentified pollen, and starch grains—all of which got into the meteorite in the laboratory.

To such arguments, NYU's George Claus and Drs. Nagy and Hennessy of Fordham University reply that their fossils were embedded in minerals indigenous to the meteorite, and earthly objects could not have worked into it that way; and that they did their analyses by means that prevented significant contamination in the laboratory.

Robert Ross of the British Museum (Natural History), London, a world-famous center of biological sciences, came into the argument on the side of the genuineness of the space fossils.

Ross said he'd found some, too.

He looked at still another fragment of the Orgueil meteorite. (Altogether, there are fifty bits of the Orgueil meteorite distributed in museums around the globe.) He discovered in it little umbrella- or mushroom-shaped objects.

If these microscopic mushrooms had been found on earth, he said, there would have been no question but that they were fossils of biotic (living) origin.

He also found other objects that somewhat resembled fossil hystrichosphaeres (tiny sea animals).

Ross said he used sterile instruments to scrape away

the surface of his piece of the Orgueil meteorite. He extracted the sample that he studied from its interior. Thus he did not risk contamination by earthly particles. They could not, he thought, have got into the meteorite's inside.

Paul Tasch of the University of Wichita has pointed out that everyone who has been heard from in the discussion about the space fossils may be correct: Some of the microfossils may be genuine plants or animals from space. Some of them may be contaminants from earth (including pollen). Some may be the result of chemical action only, not of the processes of life.

At the University of Houston not long ago, two scientists joined the search for extraterrestrial life. They started to study the Murray meteorite, which fell near Murray, Kentucky, in September 1950, and the Mokoia meteorite, which fell in Wanganui, New Zealand, in 1908. Their project, financed by the National Aeronautics and Space Administration, will run into 1965.

The men are Dr. John Oro, a biochemist, and Dr. Albert Zlatkis, a chemical engineer. They will seek chemical substances and fossils in the two meteorites. Any chemical substances they find, Drs. Oro and Zlatkis will attempt to synthesize, or create artifically, in the laboratory.

Melvin Calvin, a University of California biochemist, headed a group in Berkeley, California, that already has studied the Kentucky meteorite.

Calvin announced his results in January 1960 at the First International Space Sciences Symposium in Nice, France. In chemical analyses of the intact core of the meteorite, he had found traces of sugar acids, reducing compounds, and other materials he called "prebiotic," i.e., similar to those ancestral chemicals associated with the emergence of life on earth. The chemicals Calvin found could have helped make life possible on other worlds.

"The samples," said Calvin, "indicate that the same revolutionary processes that unfolded on earth have gone on elsewhere."

At the University of California, San Diego, Professor-at-Large Harold C. Urey, the discoverer of heavy water and a contributor to atomic energy research, is at work on the microfossils. He has been joined by Forham's Dr. Nagy.

Dr. Urey has looked at George Claus's fossils.

"The objects shown me," he said, "did indeed have the general appearance of biological material. However, I in no way regard myself as an expert in these matters."

Dr. Urey expects future experiments to produce either the final proof that the fossils and chemical compounds found in meteorites are genuinely from life, or that they are not.

The biological chemicals and tiny fossils from meteorites are the only signs of life we have from space. The tiny "fireflies" that John Glenn saw, on the first American orbital space flight, have turned out to be not "fireflies" at all. After Glenn, Scott Carpenter, the second U.S. orbital astronaut, also saw the luminous particles. They looked yellow-green—he could tap on the inside wall of his Mercury spaceship, in orbit, and flake them off. Next, Wally Schirra, on his six-orbit flight, reported the particles.

Then astronaut Gordon Cooper, on his flight of twenty-two orbits, observed the "fireflies" coming from the spacecraft's reaction-control rockets. These are little rockets used to position the Mercury spacecraft—to turn it, keep it from yawing (or wobbling), etc.

One theory is that steam from the exhaust of the rockets—steam is 54 per cent of the exhaust—can rapidly freeze into ice particles or snowflakes, the "fireflies." These flash green or yellow-green due to sunlight hitting them. This theory, says Textron's Bell Aerosystems Company, which makes the rockets, is the one that seems most probable today.

There is one other theory: that the "fireflies" come from oxygen, not steam, in the exhausts. The oxygen, ionized, hits particles of matter. A high rate of collisions, under this second theory, causes the yellow-green light.

Under either theory, the space "fireflies" are not animal but chemical, and man-made.

Philosophers in ancient Greece, at least six hundred years before Christ, speculated out loud on whether there was life on other worlds. Men have always wondered. In the nineteenth century, improved astronomical telescopes led to the discovery of straight lines on the face of the planet Mars. The lines were called canals. They caused a flurry of discussion about space life. Today some scientists believe the lines on Mars may be not canals but bands of vegetation—living matter.

In 1963, Union Carbide Company scientists reopened the talk about life on Mars. In laboratory bottles, they recreated the oxygen-argon atmosphere of Mars. In this atmosphere, they germinated seeds of marigolds, cucumbers, onions, zinnias, and other plants. Dr. Sanford Siegel of Union Carbide also determined that turtles and starfish could exist for a time in the Martian atmosphere, that a shrimp could hatch larvae in it, and that the mealworm, a beetle larva, could survive for many generations in the "Mars gas."

The nineteenth-century yak-yaking about life on other worlds reached a high point (or you might call it a low point) in 1835, when readers of the old New York *Sun* were the victims of one of the most elaborate hoaxes in history—the only major hoax in U.S. journalism. The paper fictitiously reported that an astronomer, working at the Cape of Good Hope, South Africa, had observed real life on the moon.

The stories described that life on the moon: horned sheep; gray pelicans; a ball-shaped beast that rolled across a beach; buffaloes with wool that pull down over their eyes to protect them from the sun; cranes; three-foot-long zebras; a beaver that walked on two feet, carried its young in its arms, and could build a fire; a bat-man, whose name, the *Sun* said, was "Vespertiliohomo" (man-bat)—it did not say how his name was ascertained.

The moon's mountains, lakes, and volcanic craters were described in a lot of what was alleged to be detail.

The paper's circulation zoomed from 4,000 copies a day to 20,000 on the strength of its fiction about the moon.

Today, unlike the nineteenth-century Americans who could only talk (and pull each other's legs) about life in space, we are instead getting serious.

No scientists yet have found human beings on other planets. They have not found intelligent life.

What the scientists, starting with Drs. Nagy, Meinschein, and Hennessy, have found, is that chemical compounds produced primarily by living things do exist in meteorites. By today, they have found many such significant compounds. The rug is full of bloodstains.

"When living things make compounds," Dr. Meinschein says, "they don't make just any—they make the ones they need." The relative amounts and types of carbon compound in the Orgueil meteorite and in many terrestrial sediments are similar. Therefore, on the basis of existing data, the best presumption is that living things were the source of these compounds in the meteorite as they are of these compounds on earth.

And Drs. Claus, Nagy, Hennessy, Staplin, Ross, and others have found, if their fossils are genuine, that some simple and primitive creatures are (or were) alive on other worlds. On other planets, just as on this one, simple and primitive creatures may well be associated with more complicated life.

A theory that there are 600 million planets in the Milky Way that can support life, even advanced, intelligent life, was put forward in 1963 by a Columbia University astronomer.

Professor Lloyd Motz estimated that the Milky Way, the galaxy that includes our earth, contains 200 million stars ablaze, just like our sun. "If," he said, "we suppose that the stars . . . have planetary systems like our own, we have, on the average, about three planets per star as abodes of an intelligent form of life."

The planets around each sun, he said, could be—probably are—chemically and physically equipped to support life similar to life on earth.

And beyond our Milky Way? The Mount Palomar, California, telescope, one of the huge ones, receives light from millions of galaxies. Harlow Shapley of Harvard figures there are, in these galaxies, perhaps more than ten thousand million billion stars (10 with 18 zeros) very much like our sun in size, luminosity, and chemistry, and "all radiating the kind of energy needed for photosynthesis." They could, that is, support planets—and life upon the planets.

Country after country, following the U.S. lead in the search for space life, is setting up its own programs to analyze meteorites for biological chemicals and space fossils. Sweden, Hungary, New Zealand, and half a dozen others are investigating. The U.S., Canada, and Britain, which made the first discoveries, are multiplying their efforts.

In 1962, more than one hundred U.S. scientists, having taken part in an eight-week study of the nation's space program, reported to NASA (the National Aeronautics and Space Administration):

"Of all the discoveries that have come from or can now be anticipated from man's efforts in space science, none more easily captures the imagination nor is more likely to focus interest and acclaim than the empirical proof that there is in this universe a biota [life] other than our own. . . ."

NASA plans to make probes of Mars very soon. "Puppet laboratories" sent by us to Mars may radio back their findings, and indicate whether or not there is life on that planet.

Acting on the assumption that there is life in space, the National Radio Astronomy Observatory, with its eighty-five-foot radio telescope near Green Bank, West Virginia, in 1960 began listening in one tiny arc of sky for any intelligent broadcasts that might be found amid the cacophony of cosmic sound. No results. Soon the observatory will begin again with a new 140-foot radio telescope to scan a larger part of the universe.

In addition to our radio astronomy, our Stratoscope II balloons are photographing the planets from above the earth's dust cloud. An 86-foot-tall balloon recently was sent aloft from Palestine, Texas, to a height of 100,000 feet to collect space dust—meteorite particles. The last I heard, no luck—the balloon had vanished over the Pacific. Other moon dust or space dust has been found in the snow in the Antarctic. It may contain traces of life.

The instruments in the Mariner II satellite we fired past Venus told us Venus was too hot for life as we know it.

By 1964, later experiments by Dr. Meinschein—infrared, ultraviolet, and chromatographic—gave him further evidence that he was dealing with biological (life-producing) substances in meteorites. "By the best methods we have today," he says, "we show that compounds in meteorites are similar to biological compounds on this earth."

Dr. Meinschein himself has a NASA contract for further work on the question of life outside the earth. He is developing still more ways of identifying extraterrestrial life.

"Few scientists," *The Lamp* (Standard Oil of New Jersey) explains, "expect that in the near future we shall make contact with intelligent life outside the earth, whether Martians or civilizations light-years distant beyond the solar system. What is being sought at the moment is simply chemical or biological evidence—beyond what we already have—that life exists or has existed outside the earth. . . .

"A discovery of life in outer space, supporting the meteorite investigations . . . would only confirm what many scientists now consider likely—that the whole universe is one vast laboratory of life."

This may, or may not, eventually prove true. But the traces of life already found in the Orgueil meteorite and in others—the bloodstains all over the rug—and the little fossils from space already observed under the microscope, are providing answers to questions that men have sought to answer for centuries.

"We have already learned," says Warren Meinschein, "that somewhere in outer space we may expect to find something which was, or is, life."

MANY MORE MYSTERIES

Our first information about life in space is leading to a worldwide surge of activity to obtain more information about it. In exactly the same way, the facts obtained by Charles Darwin, and by other scientists before and after him, have led—and are leading—to zoologists continuously collecting more and more facts about the animals of this world.

Yet, in spite of all we've learned, the earth, air, and sea remain full of zoological mysteries. Some are as unsolved as those of space. Here are a few of the zoological riddles —some of them being worked on, some not—to which scientists would like to know the answers.

What are the remaining unknown monsters of Africa? There may be some big animals, unknown to science, somewhere in Africa's jungles or swamps. Natives have told for years of a monster, half dragon and half elephant, that is said to dwell in the swamps and kill hippopotamuses. They call it the chipekwe. Attilio Gatti, the Italian explorer of Africa, is the only explorer I know of to speak of one unknown animal: He says that, in the Ituri forest, the Congo, there is a large, pale-faced anthropoid, something like an ape. The Ituri forest has already yielded up the okapi, the formerly unknown relative of the giraffe, and formerly unknown pygmies. It could shelter a new primate. The mountain gorilla, the biggest primate of all, was found for the first time as recently as early this century. A small primate, the dwarf chimpanzee, is quite new to men. It was discovered as recently as 1938. The smallest of all the African primates, the bush baby, or galago, could well be the object of more study. The soft-furred, owl-eyed bush baby lives in tropical forests from the Great Rift Valley to Senegal. A startling fact that is known about it is that the tiny—4 inches long—bush baby can leap six feet from a crouch.

The most intriguing of Africa's unknown creatures are little people. Two completely experienced white hunters say they have seen, amid herds of baboons, small (smaller-than-pygmy), furry, brown men. The mysterious, 4-foot-tall human-appearing creatures are called agogwe. Still other uncaught animals rumored in Africa are represented in my 1963 book, *The Maybe Monsters* (G. P. Putnam's Sons, New York).

What is the longest animal in the sea? The blue whale, at 150 to 170 tons, is certainly the heaviest; with a recorded length of 113½ feet, is it also the longest? probably not. It is, however, the longest whale by a wide margin. The fin whale, second longest, may reach 90

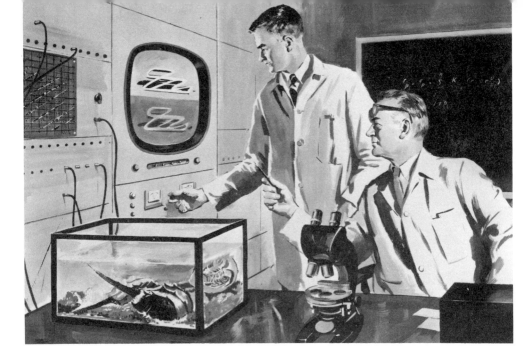

Horseshoe crab (*left*) produces two astonishing mysteries: It's found only on U. S. East Coast and in the Molucca islands. How come? Also, how can it see so well? General Electric scientists are studying it.

feet; its average length is 68 to 70 feet. In an apparent tie for third longest, the sperm whale and the Arctic right whale are recorded at 70 feet; they average around 60. The longest fishes do not compete with the blue whale in length—they are the whale sharks, 45 to 60 feet in length.

The longest sea creature could be one of the sea worms known to reach 90 feet long. There could be still longer ones we haven't found. The longest sea animal could be a giant squid, the largest cephalopod on earth. This cousin of the octopus, with ten arms instead of eight, has one pair of tentacles far longer than its other arms, and these may stretch 50 feet or—how much longer? It would help us know if we could catch giant squid, but we never have. Mrs. Diana Ross of the Peabody Museum at Yale has sent me the figures, as reported by A. E. Verrill, on a squid washed up on the shore in 1878. This was a big one, and was called the Thimble Tickle specimen. It came onto a New England beach near the village of Thimble Tickle. Its body was 20 feet long, from its tail to its big parrotlike beak, and one of its arms was 35 feet long. But the giant squid may grow far longer. Arthur Clarke, in *The Coast of Coral* (Harper, 1955), tells this story: "A few years ago, Mike [Mike Wilson, an exparatrooper] was walking along the shore of the Red Sea, near the outpost of Abu Zenima, when he came across a single rotting tentacle lying on the beach with all the sea gulls pecking at it. It was devoid of all suckers, so it must have been one of the twin arms, terminating in grasping palps, which the giant squid whips out to grasp its prey. Holding his nose, Mike paced the tentacle as accurately as he could—and he swears that it was 100 feet long."

The grown form of the 6-foot eel larva found by Anton Bruun may, of course, be well over 100 feet long. We will know if and when we catch it. Or the longest creatures in the sea may be jellyfish. The lion's mane, a stinging, mushroom-shaped jellyfish that looks something like a lion's mane, can grow into a blob of jelly 6 feet across and put out tentacles that reach 120 feet long. In one of the last of Sir Arthur Conan Doyle's stories about Sherlock Holmes, *The Adventure of the Lion's Mane,* a man is killed by this jellyfish, which does sting severely and sometimes fatally. The Portuguese man-of-war, or *Physalia,* a blue and pink iridescent jellyfish, is another candidate for the longest sea monster. Its tentacles, Ralph Buchsbaum and Lorus J. Milne report in *The Lower Animals, Living Invertebrates of the World,* may trail downward "40 to 60 feet, or perhaps even as much as 100 feet." It too can disable or kill a swimmer. The Portuguese man-of-war occurs around the world, in the Atlantic, Pacific and Indian oceans.

The giant among jellyfishes, *Cyanea arctica,* Buchsbaum and Milne write, is sometimes 8 feet across, with tentacles that hang down for 200 feet. There are no human swimmers in cold Arctic water where *Cyanea* flourishes. "So," Buchsbaum and Milne say, "we can only imagine what it would be like to be stung by such a monstrous coelenterate."

What mystery monsters dwell on top of the world's great jungles? In the 100-to-200-foot-high treetops of the great rain forests that encircle the globe, there live we know not what strange animals. The rain forests are a band, interrupted only by oceans, from the Congo through the Amazon jungles of South America, and on through New Guinea, Ceylon, southern India, and on to East Africa. They are the great lush tropical forests of the earth's belt line around the equator. Men have had no way to explore the treetops, and life there—plants, mammals, birds, snakes, toads, frogs, and insects—is still largely a mystery. There are calls from the treetops we never have connected with any known animal.

In the rich, green foliage that we cannot see through, there are primates from the beginnings of time: creatures like the potto, the ghost monkey of West Africa, with its protruding eyes that shine at night and its eery cries attributed to evil spirits; and weird, squirrel-like animals. Probably the most dangerous beast to man in the attic of the rain forest is the golden anteater, a soft, yellow, silky, fur-covered, harmless-looking, rabbit-sized creature. The golden anteater lives on termites (collected on its long, sticky tongue), it climbs leisurely, and it sits still for days at a time. But the golden anteater has sharp, scimitarlike claws with which it specializes in ripping open stomachs —a jaguar's, ocelot's, monkey's, or a man's.

Did we capture the last golden hamster? In April

The biggest beetle in the world is the size of a small rat. It's *Goliathus goliathus* of tropical Africa. It's 6 inches long, 4 inches across back. South America's Hercules beetle is about as big.

1930, a university professor in Syria dug out of a burrow thirteen golden hamsters—the first of their kind known. Since then, the descendants of the thirteen have proliferated till hamsters are found in countless schools, museums, pet stores, laboratories, homes. Not one additional wild specimen ever has been found. Incredible as it seems, it is possible that the professor-discoverer, I. Aharoni, obtained the last family of an animal on its way to extinction.

Where do the rare whales roam? The whaling industry catches whales by the thousands every year, but there are a few species of whales that we never catch because we never see them. Most are small (10- or 15-foot-long) whales. Most are beaked whales of the genus *Mesoplodon* —that means "with a tooth in the middle of the jaw." These whales apparently are among the rarest animals in the world. *Mesoplodon bowdoini* is known from only two skeletons found on the New Zealand coast. We don't even know what it looks like. *Mesoplodon stejneri* is known from only two specimens from the Pacific Coast. *Mesoplodon europaeus* is known from three, two from New Jersey, one from the English Channel. It's about 22 feet long. Of the other beaked whales, we have taken only from five to twenty-two specimens of each species. Some have been picked up in various parts of the world, others mainly around New Zealand.

Two whales—not beaked ones—that formerly were thought rare may not be.

Cuvier's whale, 26 feet long, has been seen twenty times since 1913.

The false killer whale was known for a long time only because its bones in 1846 had been dug up by Sir Richard

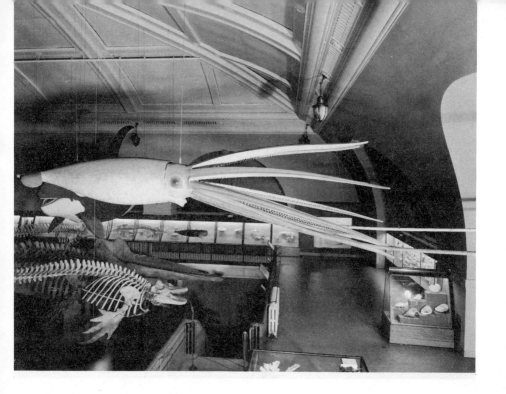

An unsolved mystery is how long the giant squid's longest arms (of its ten arms) really stretch. At least 50 feet, as this model at the American Museum of Natural History shows, maybe much farther.

Owen. Then, in 1861, a hundred false killers showed up in the Bay of Kiel, northern Germany—a hundred unknown monsters, all at once. A number ran aground, and the false killer became a familiar beast. Since then, it's disappeared, and reappeared, sometimes hundreds at once, in spots all around the globe—on the Atlantic and Pacific coasts of North and South America, on the shores of Tasmania, India, Africa, Britain.

What's the world's champion at camouflage? This might be answered if we could see easily the contending animals—which, of course, we cannot. That's the point. In 1963, the Smithsonian Institution put forth one competitor that few people know about: a green tree snake found at the Smithsonian's tropical wildlife reserve at Barro Colorado Island, Panama. "It comes," say Smithsonian people there, "about as near to being invisible as is possible for animals." The lower branches of many jungle trees are interlaced with vines. In the Panama region the vines are green all year. The snakes have about the same circumference and shade of coloring as the vines. They remain as motionless as the vines except when hunting. They hang downward just as a vine does. When, in a breeze, the vines are gently undulated, the snakes duplicate the motion of the vines in one of nature's most amazing blendings with natural surroundings.

Why do termites build skyscrapers? An amazing structure by a nonhuman builder is the 5-foot-high mound of the magnetic ant, *Hamitermes meridionalis,* a termite, of Australia. Built by termites only half an inch long, the mounds tower out of the earth in great groups, like cities, in a thirty-mile-wide patch twelve miles south of Darwin, in Australia's Northern Territory. Each mound is flattened and slablike, as are many buildings, and each lies on an exact north-and-south axis. Why are they built? We don't know. Maybe because the termites get too crowded in the ground, and, as is the case with people in a crowded city, have nowhere to build but up. We don't know why their buildings lie directly north and south. Best guess at the moment is that the skyscrapers, and their north-south axis, help the termites get coolness they need.

How did the grasshopper get there? This is a minor mystery, but it is a puzzle, just the same. During the voyage of the *Beagle,* when the ship was 370 miles off Africa, Charles Darwin saw a large grasshopper, or *Acrydium.* Now this grasshopper can neither swim nor fly far. No one ever has been able to explain how come *Acrydium* could show up far at sea. Said Darwin: "The most remarkable instance I have known of an insect being caught far from land."

How do beetles do it? Insects are the most successful animals on earth insofar as proliferating in species and numbers are concerned. This can just as well be called the age of insects as the age of man, so numerous are the bugs. Of all the insects, beetles have the most species—there are 350,000 known species and there may be a million. The beetle's is the largest of the insect orders, and may represent half of all insects. How are beetles so successful? There is no answer yet.

Beetles range in size up to the biggest, the white, red-brown, and black goliath beetle, *Goliathus goliathus,* of equatorial Africa. Goliath, 6 inches long, as large as a

Why is Peripatus found only in widely separated spots in South America, Africa, and Australia? Is it a relative of worms? No worm ever had Peripatus's hollow legs, which surprisingly end in claws.

How do the magnetic ants of Australia build skyscrapers (these tall mounds are ants' nests), and why? Why does one side of the tall structure curve in, the other side out? Do the ants plan their towns?

small rat, makes a loud whirring noise as it flies. It can break an electric light bulb by flying into it. African children make toys of goliath beetles. They tie strings on to the beetles. As the string tightens, the monster insect flies round and round in circles and makes a noise like a miniature airplane. The 6-inch Hercules beetle of South America competes with Goliath in size. U.S. beetles include May beetles and June bugs.

What came before insects? "No one," says Albro Gaul in *The Wonderful World of Insects,* "is certain . . . but there is a very interesting creature, *Peripatus,* found in South America, Africa, and Australia. It looks like a worm or a caterpillar. It has no joints on its body, but its paired rows of feet resemble to some extent the feet of insects. Internally the parts resemble the earthworm, but it breathes with tracheae like the insects; and no earthworm ever had legs. Its stubby antennae and horizontally hinged jaws are common to the insects. If there is a 'missing link' between the insects and the worms, *Peripatus* is the link."

What are the ghosts of the depths? We don't begin to know the creatures that live far beneath the surface of the sea, such as Anton Bruun's giant eel, and probably won't till our two- or three-man submarines, with windows you can look out of and lights to penetrate the blackness, become available. Until they do, we have no way of staying at the depths for any length of time. But the men who have been down have seen—what? "I have," said William Beebe, "154 separate and distinct notes on unknown fish, and 235 notes on unknown animals." Once he saw large, indistinct bodies; once, something with "six bluish-white lights along the side"; once, "hundreds of pale blue, double lights"; another time, "a luminous head"; another time, "ghostly forms in every direction." "At 2,450 [feet down] a very large creature, at least 20 feet in length, came quite near to the bathysphere," Beebe said. "I could just see its outline. Perhaps it was a porpoise or a small whale, but it may equally well have been a fish."

"Giant squid," says *Life* magazine's book, *The Sea,* "are found at 1,500 feet, and sperm whales dive that deep to eat them. There is something else, too, farther down at 3,000 feet. A sizable something that has been detected by explosive sonic methods, but nobody yet knows what it is or how big it is. So far, it is simply a squiggle on a piece of photographic paper."

Can we find out anything more about—? Practically any information would be welcome on a host of little-known creatures, the mola, or ocean sunfish, an 1,800-pound, 8-foot-long monster of the sea, for instance. (The American Museum has a 10-foot specimen.) It looks like a big, floating millstone, basks on the surface off Cuba, and dies quickly, the Miami (Florida) Seaquarium says, in its rare captivity in the U.S. Why? What about the takin, the golden gnu-goat or ox-chamois of Tibet? We don't even know what it is—an ox, sheep, goat, chamois, gnu, or musk-ox. What about the frog that attacks man, *Rana lactator,* of South America? What more can we learn about the clouded leopard of Sumatra? The civet cat, *Osbornictis piscivora,* captured just exactly once in history, by Glover A. Allen in the Congo's Ituri forest? The tapir of Sumatra? Why do tapirs exist in Latin America and in the East Indian region—and nowhere else?

The wild ox of Cambodia? Is it entirely wild or have domestic cattle contributed to it? The Asiatic lion? The American Museum, I understand, is the only one with a specimen of this rare animal. What can we find out about the pygmy water buffalo, a strong midget of Celebes? The giant rat of Liberia, Africa, 2 feet or more in length? The poisonous sea snakes of the Palau islands in the South Pacific? Or the several thousand sea snakes that, one day, Dr. Herbert Clark of the Gorgas

A view no man ever has seen in nature: head-on view of American Museum's model of giant squid. The big squid, which live 1,500 feet undersea, never have been captured by man. But sperm whales battle and eat them.

Memorial Laboratory, Balboa, Panama, found himself swimming through? What about the very rare Antarctic fox? The white-toothed cowry, a shell so rare there is one known specimen of it—in the British Museum (Natural History)? The Glory-of-the-Sea, a shell of which only twelve specimens exist? The black-shouldered opossum of Southeast Peru, which the Bronx Zoo says is the "most beautiful of American opossums" and which was unknown to exist till 1951? Of Prevost's squirrel of southeast Asia, a red, white, and blue animal? The mouse deer, a deer no bigger than a rat with hooves that won't hide a dime? The grass-cat, a little-known feline of the Pampas?

Why are there big tortoises and iguanas (both marine and land forms) in the Galápagos islands that you find nowhere else? How can the hippopotamus almost hide itself, as it can, in a pool of water only 2 feet deep? Why doesn't the hippo squash its babies as it wallows in a river? How does the albatross rest? It is a bird that cannot perch. What does the albatross do in a gale—ride out the storm on the water? How could it? How does the megapode, a 3-pound bird, lay an egg the size of a grapefruit? Why do some sharks attack you, while others turn away from you?

What makes a lion, tiger, or leopard turn into a man-eater? One theory has been that it's wounds or crippling injuries or old age that prevent the beast chasing its usual game; this theory now is losing support. Where do tuna spawn? Why does the narwhal have that long, slender, unicornlike horn (and in a few cases, two of them)? We have no idea. Why does the firefish, *Pterois volitans,* cause such great pain? An Arab said after it had stung him he was in such agony that his friends had to tie him up to keep him from hurling himself into the sea. What is the Irukandji (an aboriginal name)—an animal, unseen and unidentified, that stings swimmers in Australia, and causes them, five to sixty minutes later, to collapse in intense pain and vomit violently? There have been hundreds of persons stung by Irukandji during the Australian summer, December-February. Not even fine-meshed nets ever have caught it. And what can we learn of the even more dreadful sea wasp, *Chiropsalmus quadrigatus,* another menace to Australian bathers? The sea wasp stings people in shallow water. A victim staggers ashore, and dies in three to eight or ten minutes. About all that is known of the sea wasp is that it is *not* the Portuguese man-of-war, and that its poison is more deadly than any known snake poison.

There is a sea creature that is a ball, a little smaller than a ping-pong ball. It's called *Plankto-sphaera.* It is transparent. We cannot fit it into any group of animals we know. It is an almost total mystery. It is being studied now, as are all the mysteries that follow.

How do some animals see better than we do? In the Himalaya mountains, men come upon mysterious footprints in the snow—manlike tracks. They never have captured the animal—or man—that makes them. So they nicknamed him the Abominable Snowman. Natives call him the yeti. Norman Dyhrenfurth, leader of the 1963 U.S. expedition that performed the incredible feat of sending six men to the summit of the world's highest mountain, Everest, kept an eye peeled for the Snowman. Dyhrenfurth tells me he believes in the yeti, but he did not see him. One reason the Snowman, or yeti, can keep away may be that he has better eyes and longer distance vision than we have and thus sees us much further away than we can see him.

Other animals also are known to see better, in one way or other, and men would like to know how. One animal that does is the horseshoe crab. This animal, *Limulus polyphemus,* is called by the National Geographic Society one of the oddest creatures known to science. It is a distant relative of spiders and scorpions, is 2 feet long, has six pairs of claw-tipped legs, and a daggerlike tail. It lives in the Atlantic from Maine to Yucatán, especially at the mouth of the Delaware River between New Jersey and Pennsylvania. Its protruding eyes, simple in design, are being studied by the General Electric Company, object: to learn how to make electronic computers "see," to teach the machines to read, and therefore to do complex tasks. The horseshoe crab's eyesight could lead, G.E. says, to a sensing and guiding mechanism to take our unmanned space vehicles to the moon and the planets. It's all part of the new science of bionics, joining the principles of biology and electronics.

How do fish sleep? A step toward getting an answer came from University of Wisconsin scientists. They noticed that, at dusk, schools of perch disappeared from an echo sounder that, in the daytime, kept the perch located. A diver went down at night with an undersea flashlight. He found thousands of fish resting on the bottom. As the light disturbed them, they swam off a little and lay down again for further snoozing. Much work needs to be done before we know how fish and sea-dwelling animals rest and sleep.

How do penguins get home? The migration of birds, across oceans and hemispheres, is one of the wonders of natural history. It involves ability on the part of the birds to navigate—and we do not know the mechanism. Scientists cannot themselves hop into the air and fly, and therefore would have a hard time following the birds to learn how they navigate. But penguins are birds that do not fly—they cannot—yet do have the ability to get home across long distances.

So in 1962-1963, the U.S. Navy flew some scientists

and Adelie penguins to a point 660 miles inside the Antarctic. There, John T. Emlen, Jr., and Richard L. Penney, of the University of Wisconsin, turned loose the penguins and followed them as they headed north toward the coast. The men walked or rode little motor toboggans. The penguins also walked or tobogganed. Tobogganing, to a penguin, is flopping down on his stomach, digging in with his toes, and scooting along the ice at up to 8 miles an hour. This burst of speed doesn't last; the penguins averaged, en route home, 6 to 8 miles a day, the men learned.

A big problem: lots of the time the penguins spent just sitting, and there was nothing Emlen and Penney could do about it—except sit still themselves in minus-46-degree cold. Their conclusion: the penguins use the sun as a navigational aid in homing—but they also have an "internal clock" to help, too, and we don't understand that yet. More work is needed.

How does the frog-eating crab survive? In Thailand (formerly Siam), there is a frog-eating crab so important that it is attracting all at once the attention of the National Science Foundation, the U.S. Navy, Columbia University and its Lamont Observatory and its director Maurice Ewing, and Malcolm Gordon of the University of California at Los Angeles. The point of the curiosity of all these experts: they want to know how come the Siamese crab can survive in both fresh and salt water. This is a difficult trick, though some creatures, like sturgeon and salmon, manage it. The ordinary lobster dies in fresh water. The frog-eating crab can provide us with valuable scientific knowledge.

Why do some areas of the sea produce monsters?

Several places in the ocean have been located that, entirely mysteriously, seem to keep their inhabitants free of germs and to cause them to grow into monster size. One such area, in the Pacific, reaches from Panama up along the coast of Mexico. Here marlin, whose normal weight in other seas is 250 pounds, grow into 2,500-pound monsters. Here the yellowtail, off California usually only 20 pounds, grow to over 100 pounds. Here algae (sea plants) reach several hundred yards long and grow "trunks" like trees, over 3 feet thick. The area is being studied; so far about all we know is that the fish from this spot are remarkably free of poisonous bacteria or parasites.

How much life is there at the greatest depths of the sea? Men have only been there once, for a short time, and therefore we do not know. On January 23, 1960, the U.S. Navy lowered its bathyscaphe, the *Trieste,* with Jacques Piccard and Lieutenant Donald Walsh aboard, 35,300 feet down in the Challenger deep of the Marianas trench in the Pacific. In twenty minutes on the bottom, the divers saw a fish a foot long, something like a sole. They saw a "beautiful red shrimp" an inch long. "Here, in an instant," said Piccard, "was the answer that biologists had asked for [for] decades. Could life exist in the greatest depths of the ocean? It could!" "Staggeringly lucky," Lieutenant Walsh called it, for the men to see two animals in their short stay. How much more life there is on the deepest sea bed, and its nature, is still unknown.

How much life in the Antarctic ice? Believe it or not, a Navy doctor, Lieutenant Sidney Tolchin of Easton, Pennsylvania, took a sample of ice from a hundred feet down, looked at it under a microscope, and found—life.

He saw staphylococci, bacteria dangerous to man. Warmed up, they became active and began to multiply. "The questions," says Roger A. Caras in *Antarctica: Land of Frozen Time,* "that spring from this discovery are almost overwhelming. How did the germs get there? How long had they been there? How did they survive an average temperature of 65 degrees below zero for a century or, perhaps, many centuries? Most intriguing of all —if these specks of life can survive, can others? Will deep cores bring up prehistoric life forms that have lain dormant in a kind of icy time capsule? Will future exploration into the heart of the ice produce eggs that can be hatched to release, in this day and age, prehistoric forms of animal life?"

By today, we know that life—tiny spiders—exists on the world's highest mountains, and we have seen two fish on the deepest floor of the sea. Life occupies nearly every niche on earth. By today, we know life may well exist, and thrive, on other planets. But with all our knowledge, there are monsters on this planet we have not even identified. And whenever we find an unsuspected animal, like the Antarctic bacteria, it raises more questions than we can yet answer.

"Can we suppose that we have at all exhausted the great museum of nature?" Charles Gould asks in *Mythical Monsters.* He answers his own question with another one: "Have we, in fact, penetrated yet beyond its antechambers?"

BIBLIOGRAPHY

CHAPTER I
Darwin, Charles, *Journal of Researches . . . Voyage of H.M.S. Beagle*. The Heritage Press, New York, 1957.
"Jam of Scientists Seek Jelly Monster," New York *World-Telegram & Sun*, August 22, 1963.

CHAPTER II
Robertson, R. B., *Of Whales and Men*. Alfred A. Knopf, New York, 1954.
Slijper, E. J., *Whales*. Basic Books, Inc., New York, 1962.
Winston, Lt. Col. Waldon C., "The Largest Whale Ever Weighed," *Natural History*, Nov., 1950, pp. 393-99.

CHAPTER III
Akeley, Carl, and Jobe, Mary L., *Lions, Gorillas, and Their Neighbors*. Dodd, Mead & Company, New York, 1932.
Beatty, Bill, *Unique to Australia*. Angus and Robertson, 1962.
Bourlière, François, *Mammals of the World*. Alfred A. Knopf, New York, 1955.
Cotlow, Lewis, *Zanzabuku*. Rinehart & Company, Inc., New York, 1956.
Dinesen, Isak, *Out of Africa*. The Modern Library, New York, 1952.
Foran, W. Robert, *A Breath of the Wilds*. Robert Hale Limited, London, 1958.
Hillaby, John, "A Naturalist in the Congo," *The Listener*, Jan. 16, 1958, pp. 101-02.
Hubbard, Wynant Davis, *Wild Animal Hunter*. Harper & Brothers, New York, 1958.
Lake, Alexander, *Hunter's Choice*. Doubleday & Company, Inc., New York, 1954.
Molloy, Peter, *The Cry of the Fish Eagle*. Michael Joseph, London, 1957.
Papashvily, George and Helen, *Dogs and People*. J. P. Lippincott Company, Philadelphia, 1954.
Roosevelt, Theodore, *African Game Trails*. Charles Scribners' Sons, New York, 1909.
Simon, Noel, *Between the Sunlight and the Thunder*. Houghton Mifflin Company, Boston, 1963.

Smith, T. Murray, *The Nature of the Beast.* Coward-McCann, Inc., New York, 1963.
Spinage, C. A., *Animals of East Africa.* Houghton Mifflin Company, Boston, 1963.
Taylor, John, *Pondoro, Last of the Ivory Hunters.* Simon and Schuster, New York, 1955.

CHAPTER IV
Breland, Osmond P., *Animal Facts and Fallacies.* Harper & Brothers, New York, 1948. (Pirarucu—arapaima)
Burton, Maurice, *Story of Animal Life.* Elsevier, London, 1949. (Gar fishes)
Herald, Earl S., *Living Fishes of the World.* Doubleday & Company, Inc., New York, 1961. (Gar fishes)
National Geographic Society, *The Book of Fishes.* Washington, D.C., 1952, 1958. (Alligator gar and sturgeon)
Norman, J. R., and Fraser, F. C., *Giant Fishes, Whales and Dolphins.* W. W. Norton, New York, 1938. (Sturgeon)
The Flathead Courier, various dates, Paul H. Fugleberg, editor.

CHAPTER V
Barrett, Charles, *An Australian Animal Book.* Oxford University Press, Melbourne, Wellington, 1955.
Burton, Maurice, *Story of Animal Life.* Elsevier, London, 1949.
People (an Australian newspaper), Jan. 4, 1961.
Tate, G. H. H., "Mammals of Cape York Peninsula," *Bull. Amer. Nat. Hist.,* New York, 1952, pp. 563-616.
Troughton, Ellis, *Furred Animals of Australia.* Angus & Robertson, Sydney, London, 1951.

CHAPTER VI
Crompton, John, *The Living Sea.* Doubleday & Company, Inc., New York, 1957.
Merriman, Daniel, "Yale and the Sea," *Yale Alumni Magazine,* Oct., 1963, pp. 7-21.
National Geographic Society, *The Book of Fishes.* Washington, D.C., 1924.
Norman, J. R., and Fraser, F. C., *Giant Fishes, Whales and Dolphins.* W. W. Norton, New York, 1938.

CHAPTER VII
Smith Kline and French Laboratories, News Release.
The National Observer, Washington, D.C., Feb. 18, 1963.
The Sunday Bulletin, Philadelphia, Jan. 27, 1963.

CHAPTER VIII
Coates, Christopher, "Kick of an Electric Eel," *Atlantic Monthly,* Oct., 1947.

Nachmansohn, David, "Electric Currents in Nerve Tissue and Electric Organs," *Electric Engineering*, March, 1950.

Up De Graff, F. W., *Head Hunters of the Amazon*. Duffield and Company, New York, 1923.

CHAPTER IX

Fleay, David, and Breeden, Stanley, "Strange Animals of the Island Continent," *National Geographic*, Sept., 1963.

Wilkinson, H. E., "The Rediscovery of Leadbeater's Possum,"*. Victoria Naturalist*, August, 1961, pp. 97-102.

CHAPTER X

Bellomy, M. D., "The Fish That Is All Head," *Sea Frontiers*, Feb., 1961, pp. 12-18. (Sunfish)

Breland, Osmond P., *Animal Life and Lore*. Harper & Row, New York, 1963. (Sunfish)

Burton, Maurice, "The Soay Beast," *The Illustrated London News*, June 4, 1960, pp. 972-73; Oct. 19, 1961, p. 637.

Crompton, John, *The Living Sea*. Doubleday & Company, Inc., New York, 1957. (Killer whale)

Fraser, James, *Nature Adrift*. Philadelphia Dufour Editions, 1962. (Sunfish)

Maxwell, Gavin, *Ring of Bright Water*. E. P. Dutton & Co., Inc., New York, 1961.

National Science Foundation, "Sea Turtles Provide Clues to Understanding Animal Orientation," News Release NSF-62-142, Sept. 16, 1962. (Green turtle)

CHAPTER XI

Australian Museum Magazine, June 15, 1958.

Barrett, Charles, in the *Bulletin of the N. Y. Zoological Society*, March-April, 1938.

Bellomy, Mildred, *Illustrated Library of Natural History*, Vol. II, p. 897.

CHAPTER XII

Burton, Maurice, *Animal Legends*. Coward-McCann, Inc., New York, 1957.

Pinkerton, Robert E., *Nature Roundup*. Harper & Brothers, New York, 1955.

"Possibility of Sea Serpent Seen by Danish Scientist," San Francisco *Examiner*, April 7, 1952.

"Scientist Backs Up Monster Fish Tale—Believes Huge Serpents Exist in Great Depths," *New York Times*, Aug. 10, 1953.

"Sea Serpent Giant Eel," *Time* magazine, April 21, 1952.

Spink, Reginald, *Galathea, Deep Sea Expedition 1950-52*. George Allen and Unwin, Ltd., London, 1956.

BIBLIOGRAPHY

CHAPTER XIII
Buchsbaum, Ralph, and Milne, Lorus J., *The Lower Animals, Living Invertebrates of the World*. Doubleday & Company, Inc., New York, 1960.
Chapman, Wilbert M., *Fishing in Troubled Waters*. J. B. Lippincott Company, Philadelphia, 1949.
Hass, Hans, *We Come from the Sea*. Doubleday & Company, Inc., New York, 1959.
Henry, Thomas R., *The Strangest Things in the World*. Public Affairs Press, Washington, D.C., 1958.
Verrill, A. Hyatt, *Strange Sea Shells and Their Stories*. Grosset & Dunlap, New York, 1936.

CHAPTER XIV
Annals of the New York Academy of Sciences, Vol. 108, Art. 2, June 29, 1963, pp. 339-616.
"Like Nothing on Earth," *The Lamp*, Summer, 1962, Standard Oil Company, N.J., pp. 16-21.
"To Find Fresh Proof of Life in Space," *The Lamp*, Spring, 1963, Standard Oil Company, N.J., pp. 20-21.

CHAPTER XV
Gaul, Albro, *The Wonderful World of Insects*. Holt, Rinehart and Winston, New York, 1953. (Peripatus)
Hass, Hans, *We Come from the Sea*. Doubleday & Company, Inc., New York, 1959. (Sea wasps)
Street, Philip, *Vanishing Animals*. E. P. Dutton & Co., Inc., New York, 1963. (Golden hamster)
Troebst, Cord-Christian, *Conquest of the Sea*. Harper & Row, New York, 1962. (Walsh and Piccard at bottom of sea)
University of Wisconsin news release Feb. 7, 1963. (Emlen, Penny and the penguins)

The Author

GARDNER SOULE is a diligent searcher who has fascinated millions of readers with his newspaper and magazine features on unusual and mythological creatures. A former magazine editor, he now devotes most of his time and energy to culling from museums, explorers, and other sources of natural lore all factual information gathered on the vast number of creatures which stir a man's curiosity or credulity. He is the author of *The Maybe Monsters,* published by Putnam.